OUR WORLD TODAY

People, Places, and Issues

Daily Focus Skills
Transparencies
Sampler

Mc Graw Hill **Glencoe McGraw-Hill**

New York, New York   Columbus, Ohio   Chicago, Illinois   Peoria, Illinois   Woodland Hills, California

Glencoe/McGraw-Hill

*A Division of The **McGraw·Hill** Companies*

Printed in the United States of America.

Send all inquiries to:
Glencoe/McGraw-Hill
8787 Orion Place
Columbus, Ohio 43240-4027

ISBN 0-07-831130-6

063

DAILY FOCUS SKILLS TRANSPARENCIES

The **Daily Focus Skills Transparencies** are one of three transparency binders that enhance and expand the content found in the student edition of *Our World Today.* The Daily Focus Skills Transparencies have a twofold purpose. First, each transparency corresponds to a section of the student edition. The content on the transparency reinforces or highlights information in each section, so the transparency serves as a lesson warm-up or bellringer activity. Second, each transparency focuses on a skill used every day in Social Studies and is often found on proficiency and standardized tests. Consistent and frequent practice enables students to master these important skills.

The *Daily Focus Skills Blackline Masters* include all of the Daily Focus Skills Transparencies in reproducible form. *Daily Focus Skills Blackline Masters* are designed to help teachers introduce each section of *Our World Today,* and they contain a question that students can answer as they study the transparency or blackline master. Each page starts with a prompt—a visual, graphic, photograph, and/or quote. The question in standardized test format follows that prompt.

Turn the page to view reduced samples of **ALL** 67 Daily Focus Skills Transparencies and Blackline Masters for *Our World Today.*

Unit 1

Section 1-1

UNIT 1 | **DAILY FOCUS SKILLS**
Chapter 1 | **TRANSPARENCY 1-1**

ANSWER: Birthrates will exceed death rates in Africa and Latin America; this will not occur in Asia, Europe, North America, and Australia/Oceania.

Teacher Tip: Tell students that percentages allow them to compare relative changes in population.

Drawing Conclusions

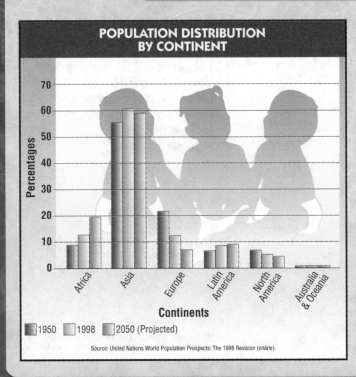

POPULATION DISTRIBUTION BY CONTINENT

Percentages

Continents

1950 1998 2050 (Projected)

Source: United Nations World Population Prospects: The 1998 Revision (online).

Directions: Answer the following question based on the bar graph.

Populations increase when the birthrate is greater than the death rate. What can you conclude about the projected birthrate and death rate for each continent from now to 2050?

_____

_____

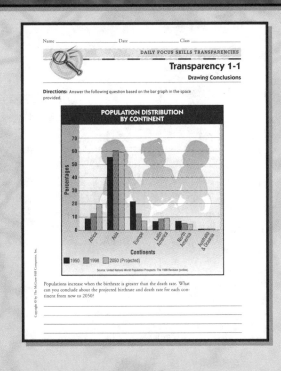

Unit 1

Section 1-2

UNIT 1 | **DAILY FOCUS SKILLS**
Chapter 1 | **TRANSPARENCY 1-2**

ANSWER: C

Teacher Tip: Encourage students to read the answer options carefully. Although Finland has a larger percentage than Sweden, it is not an answer option.

Interpreting Bar Graphs

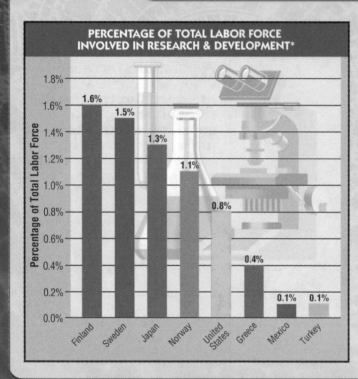

PERCENTAGE OF TOTAL LABOR FORCE INVOLVED IN RESEARCH & DEVELOPMENT*

Directions: Answer the following question based on the bar graph.

Which of the following countries has the largest percentage of its labor force working in research and development?

A Greece

B Japan

C Sweden

D Turkey

*Research & Development employees create new products and improve existing products.

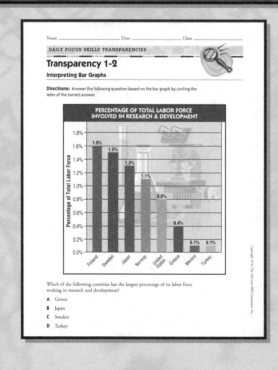

Name _____ Date _____ Class _____

DAILY FOCUS SKILLS TRANSPARENCIES

Transparency 1-2

Interpreting Bar Graphs

Directions: Answer the following question based on the bar graph by circling the letter of the correct answer.

PERCENTAGE OF TOTAL LABOR FORCE INVOLVED IN RESEARCH & DEVELOPMENT

Which of the following countries has the largest percentage of its labor force working in research and development?

A Greece
B Japan
C Sweden
D Turkey

Unit 1

Section 1-3

UNIT 1 | **DAILY FOCUS SKILLS**
Chapter 1 | **TRANSPARENCY 1-3**

ANSWER: C

Teacher Tip: Explain to students that refugees are people who leave their own country to escape danger or natural disasters.

Interpreting Maps

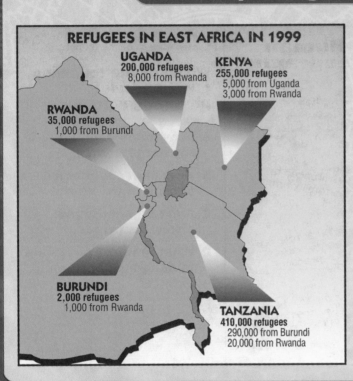

REFUGEES IN EAST AFRICA IN 1999

UGANDA
200,000 refugees
8,000 from Rwanda

KENYA
255,000 refugees
5,000 from Uganda
3,000 from Rwanda

RWANDA
35,000 refugees
1,000 from Burundi

BURUNDI
2,000 refugees
1,000 from Rwanda

TANZANIA
410,000 refugees
290,000 from Burundi
20,000 from Rwanda

Directions: Answer the following question based on the map.

Which country has the greatest number of refugees from Rwanda?

A Burundi

B Kenya

C Tanzania

D Uganda

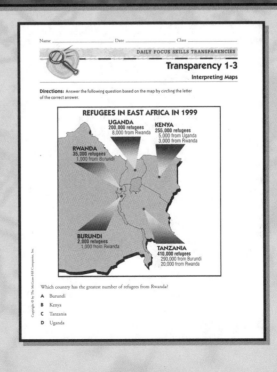

Name _____ Date _____ Class _____

DAILY FOCUS SKILLS TRANSPARENCIES

Transparency 1-3
Interpreting Maps

Directions: Answer the following question based on the map by circling the letter of the correct answer.

REFUGEES IN EAST AFRICA IN 1999

UGANDA
200,000 refugees
8,000 from Rwanda

KENYA
255,000 refugees
5,000 from Uganda
3,000 from Rwanda

RWANDA
35,000 refugees
1,000 from Burundi

BURUNDI
2,000 refugees
1,000 from Rwanda

TANZANIA
410,000 refugees
290,000 from Burundi
20,000 from Rwanda

Which country has the greatest number of refugees from Rwanda?

A Burundi

B Kenya

C Tanzania

D Uganda

Unit 1

Section 2-1

UNIT 1 | **DAILY FOCUS SKILLS**
Chapter 2 | **TRANSPARENCY 2-1**

ANSWER: D

Teacher Tip: Explain to students that physical and human geography work together to help us understand our world.

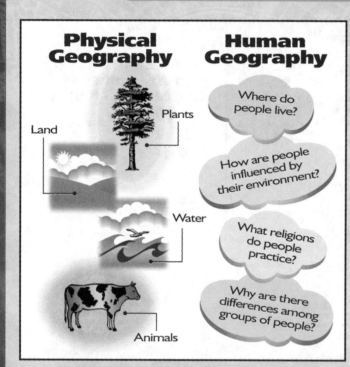

Comparing and Contrasting

Physical Geography

- Plants
- Land
- Water
- Animals

Human Geography

- Where do people live?
- How are people influenced by their environment?
- What religions do people practice?
- Why are there differences among groups of people?

Directions: Answer the following question based on the graphic.

Which of the following questions relate to physical geography?

A How many people live in my hometown?

B How many languages are spoken in the world?

C From where did my ancestors come?

D What kinds of plants are in danger of becoming extinct?

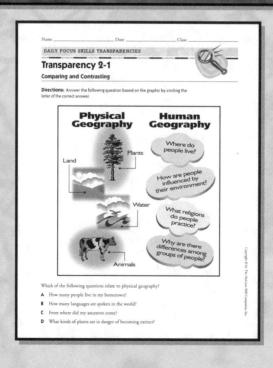

Name _____ Date _____ Class _____

DAILY FOCUS SKILLS TRANSPARENCIES

Transparency 2-1

Comparing and Contrasting

Directions: Answer the following question based on the graphic by circling the letter of the correct answer.

Physical Geography

- Plants
- Land
- Water
- Animals

Human Geography

- Where do people live?
- How are people influenced by their environment?
- What religions do people practice?
- Why are there differences among groups of people?

Which of the following questions relate to physical geography?

A How many people live in my hometown?

B How many languages are spoken in the world?

C From where did my ancestors come?

D What kinds of plants are in danger of becoming extinct?

Section 2-2

UNIT 1 | **DAILY FOCUS SKILLS**
Chapter 2 | **TRANSPARENCY 2-2**

ANSWER: A

Teacher Tip: Explain to students that they must read the question carefully when analyzing statistics. Tell them to look for key words such as MOST or LEAST.

Analyzing Statistics

Measuring an Earthquake

The Richter scale measures the size, or magnitude, of an earthquake. Each 1.0 point increase on the scale means that the size of the earthquake increases by a factor of more than 30. A 6.0 earthquake is more than 30 times stronger than a 5.0 earthquake. A 7.0 earthquake is more than 900 times stronger than a 5.0 earthquake.

Average Annual Earthquakes
Worldwide During the 20th Century

Richter Scale Measurement	Annual Number of Earthquakes
5.0 – 5.9	800
6.0 – 6.9	120
7.0 – 7.9	18
8.0 or greater	1

Directions: Answer the following question based on the chart.

Which magnitude of earthquake occurs most often?

A 5.0–5.9

B 6.0–6.9

C 7.0–7.9

D 8.0 or greater

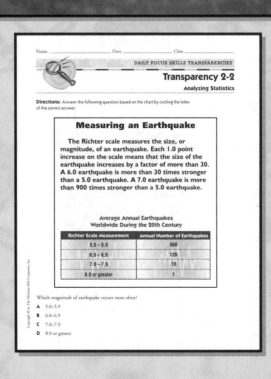

Name _____ Date _____ Class _____

DAILY FOCUS SKILLS TRANSPARENCIES

Transparency 2-2
Analyzing Statistics

Directions: Answer the following question based on the chart by circling the letter of the correct answer.

Measuring an Earthquake

The Richter scale measures the size, or magnitude, of an earthquake. Each 1.0 point increase on the scale means that the size of the earthquake increases by a factor of more than 30. A 6.0 earthquake is more than 30 times stronger than a 5.0 earthquake. A 7.0 earthquake is more than 900 times stronger than a 5.0 earthquake.

Average Annual Earthquakes
Worldwide During the 20th Century

Richter Scale Measurement	Annual Number of Earthquakes
5.0 – 5.9	800
6.0 – 6.9	120
7.0 – 7.9	18
8.0 or greater	1

Which magnitude of earthquake occurs most often?

A 5.0–5.9

B 6.0–6.9

C 7.0–7.9

D 8.0 or greater

Copyright © by The McGraw-Hill Companies, Inc.

Unit 1

Section 2-3

UNIT 1 | **DAILY FOCUS SKILLS**
Chapter 2 | **TRANSPARENCY 2-3**

ANSWER: B

Teacher Tip: Explain to students that the pictures and the words work together to express a political or social message.

Interpreting Social and Political Messages of Cartoons

"They have very strict anti-pollution laws in this state."

Directions: Answer the following question based on the cartoon.

What does the cartoon imply about pollution laws?

A They are unnecessary.

B They help keep the air clean.

C They do not work.

D They damage the environment.

This full-sized transparency is included in this Sampler!

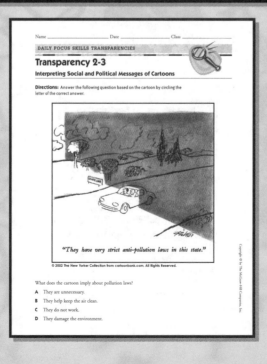

Name _____ Date _____ Class _____

DAILY FOCUS SKILLS TRANSPARENCIES

Transparency 2-3

Interpreting Social and Political Messages of Cartoons

Directions: Answer the following question based on the cartoon by circling the letter of the correct answer.

"They have very strict anti-pollution laws in this state."

© 2002 The New Yorker Collection from cartoonbank.com. All Rights Reserved.

What does the cartoon imply about pollution laws?

A They are unnecessary.

B They help keep the air clean.

C They do not work.

D They damage the environment.

Copyright © by The McGraw-Hill Companies, Inc.

Unit 2

Section 3-1

UNIT 2 | **DAILY FOCUS SKILLS**
Chapter 3 | **TRANSPARENCY 3-1**

ANSWER: D

Teacher Tip: Tell students that they should identify the starting and ending point of a time line to understand the time period covered.

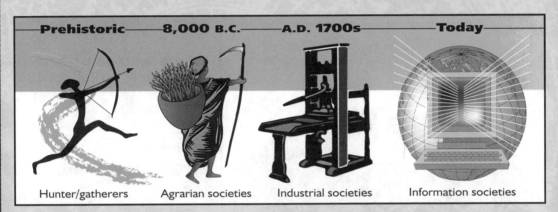

Interpreting Time Lines

Prehistoric — 8,000 B.C. — A.D. 1700s — Today

Hunter/gatherers   Agrarian societies   Industrial societies   Information societies

Directions: Answer the following question based on the time line.

How did the earliest humans get food?

A They grew it.

B They ordered it from the Internet.

C They bought it from stores.

D They hunted meat and gathered fruits and vegetables.

This full-sized transparency is included in this Sampler!

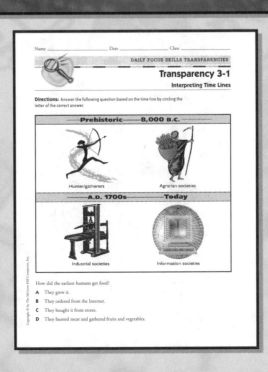

Name _____ Date _____ Class _____

DAILY FOCUS SKILLS TRANSPARENCIES

Transparency 3-1

Interpreting Time Lines

Directions: Answer the following question based on the time line by circling the letter of the correct answer.

Prehistoric — 8,000 B.C.

Hunter/gatherers   Agrarian societies

A.D. 1700s — Today

Industrial societies   Information societies

How did the earliest humans get food?

A They grew it.

B They ordered from the Internet.

C They bought it from stores.

D They hunted meat and gathered fruits and vegetables.

Unit 2

UNIT 2 | **DAILY FOCUS SKILLS**
Chapter 3 | **TRANSPARENCY 3-2**

ANSWER: C

Teacher Tip: Have students read the labels and compare the segments of the graph. Tell students that the Law of Return allows Jews living anywhere in the world to come to Israel to live.

Interpreting Circle Graphs

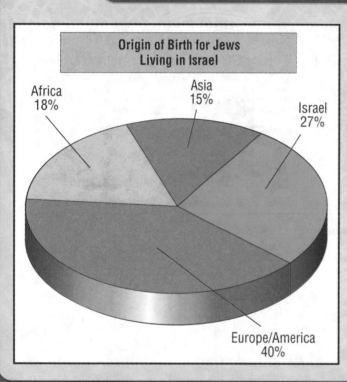

Origin of Birth for Jews Living in Israel

Africa 18%
Asia 15%
Israel 27%
Europe/America 40%

Directions: Answer the following question based on the circle graph.

Where were most Jews who live in Israel today born?

A Asia

B Africa

C Europe and America

D Israel

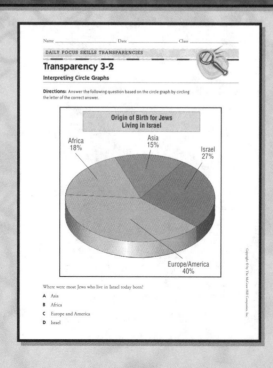

Name _____ Date _____ Class _____

DAILY FOCUS SKILLS TRANSPARENCIES

Transparency 3-2

Interpreting Circle Graphs

Directions: Answer the following question based on the circle graph by circling the letter of the correct answer.

Origin of Birth for Jews Living in Israel

Africa 18%
Asia 15%
Israel 27%
Europe/America 40%

Where were most Jews who live in Israel today born?

A Asia

B Africa

C Europe and America

D Israel

Unit 2

Section 4-1

UNIT 2 | **DAILY FOCUS SKILLS**
Chapter 4 | **TRANSPARENCY 4-1**

ANSWER: B

Teacher Tip: Remind students to read the question and all answer choices carefully before answering the question.

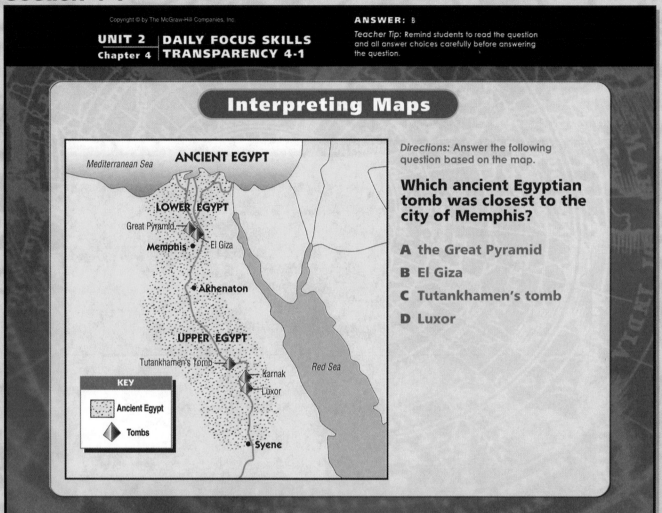

Interpreting Maps

ANCIENT EGYPT

Mediterranean Sea

LOWER EGYPT

Great Pyramid

Memphis • — El Giza

• **Akhenaton**

UPPER EGYPT

Tutankhamen's Tomb

• Karnak

Luxor

Red Sea

• **Syene**

KEY

Ancient Egypt

Tombs

Directions: Answer the following question based on the map.

Which ancient Egyptian tomb was closest to the city of Memphis?

A the Great Pyramid

B El Giza

C Tutankhamen's tomb

D Luxor

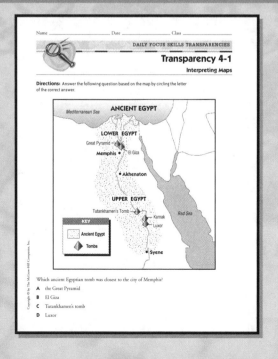

Name _____ Date _____ Class _____

DAILY FOCUS SKILLS TRANSPARENCIES

Transparency 4-1

Interpreting Maps

Directions: Answer the following question based on the map by circling the letter of the correct answer.

ANCIENT EGYPT

Mediterranean Sea

LOWER EGYPT

Great Pyramid

Memphis • El Giza

• **Akhenaton**

UPPER EGYPT

Tutankhamen's Tomb

Karnak

Luxor

Red Sea

• **Syene**

KEY

Ancient Egypt

Tombs

Which ancient Egyptian tomb was closest to the city of Memphis?

A the Great Pyramid

B El Giza

C Tutankhamen's tomb

D Luxor

Unit 2

Section 4-2

UNIT 2 | **DAILY FOCUS SKILLS**
Chapter 4 | **TRANSPARENCY 4-2**

ANSWER: D

Teacher Tip: Explain to students that each of the earthquakes along the fault left visible cracks in the earth's surface. The map shows which earthquake caused these surface ruptures.

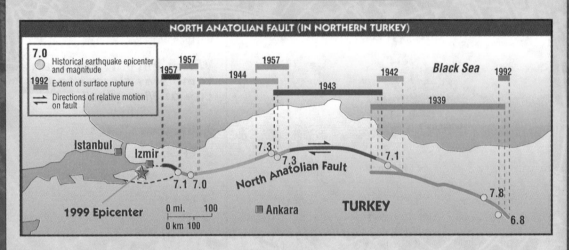

Interpreting Maps

NORTH ANATOLIAN FAULT (IN NORTHERN TURKEY)

Directions: Answer the following question based on the map.

Which earthquake caused the largest crack in the earth's surface?

A 1999

B 1944

C 1943

D 1939

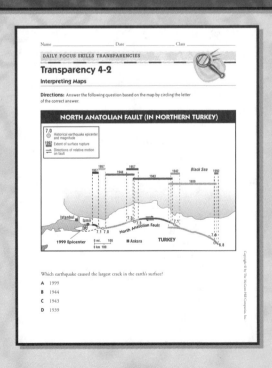

Unit 2

UNIT 2 | **DAILY FOCUS SKILLS**
Chapter 4 | **TRANSPARENCY 4-3**

ANSWER: In the Bedouin culture men and women lead somewhat separate lives. Women do not travel alone. When guests arrive, they will likely be men.

Teacher Tip: Remind students that a hypothesis is an educated guess based on the facts presented.

Forming Hypotheses

The Bedouin Tent

mag'ad
or sitting place
for men
entertaining guests

ma'had
woven curtain

maharama
or place
for
women

Directions: Answer the following question based on the information in the illustration.

Why do you think the *mag'ad* is used by only men and guests?

_____

_____

_____

_____

Name _____ Date _____ Class _____

DAILY FOCUS SKILLS TRANSPARENCIES

Transparency 4-3
Forming Hypotheses

Directions: Answer the following question based on the information in the illustration in the space provided.

The Bedouin Tent

mag'ad
or sitting place
for men
entertaining guests

ma'had
woven curtain

maharama
or place
for
women

Why do you think the *mag'ad* is used by only men and guests?

_____

_____

_____

Unit 2

Section 4-4

UNIT 2 | **DAILY FOCUS SKILLS**
Chapter 4 | **TRANSPARENCY 4-4**

ANSWER: C

Teacher Tip: Remind students that each set of bars represents the percentages for an individual country.

Interpreting Bar Graphs

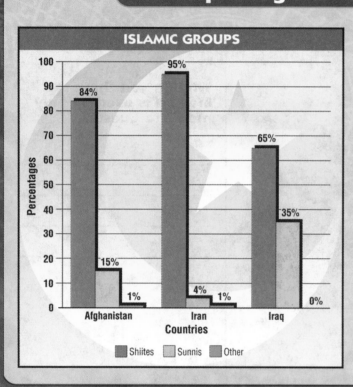

ISLAMIC GROUPS

Directions: Answer the following question based on the information in the bar graph.

What percentage of Muslims in Iraq are Sunnis?

A 95 percent

B 65 percent

C 35 percent

D 4 percent

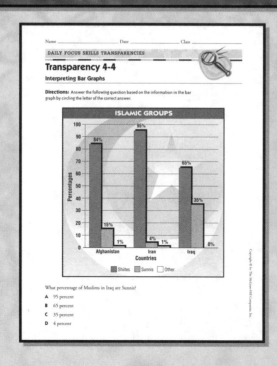

Unit 3

UNIT 3 | **DAILY FOCUS SKILLS**
Chapter 5 | **TRANSPARENCY 5-1**

ANSWER: Hindu, Muslim, and Christian religions are widely followed in India.

Teacher Tip: Tell students that a generalization is a broad statement based on observations and facts.

Making Generalizations

Official Holidays in India		≋ State	☪ Muslim	🕉 Hindu	✝ Christian

January 26	Republic Day	≋	in May	Buddha Purnima	🕉
in February	End of Ramadan	☪	in July	Birth of the Prophet	☪
in March	Holi	🕉	in August	Janmashtami	🕉
in March or April	Ram Navami and Mahabir Jayanti	🕉	August 15	Independence Day	≋
in March or April	Good Friday and Easter Monday	✝	in October or November	Dussehra, Diwali, and Guru Nanak's Birthday	🕉
in April	Feast of Sacrifice	☪	October 2	Mohandas Gandhi's Birthday	≋
in April or May	Islamic New Year	☪	December 25-26	Christmas	✝

Directions: Answer the following question based on the information presented.

What religions are widely followed in India? Explain.

_____

_____

This full-sized transparency is included in this Sampler!

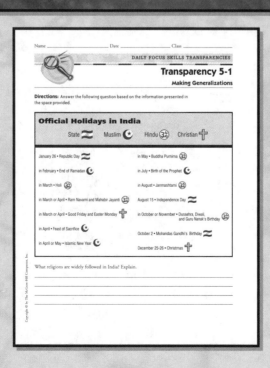

Unit 3

Section 5-2

UNIT 3 | **DAILY FOCUS SKILLS**
Chapter 5 | **TRANSPARENCY 5-2**

ANSWER: D

Teacher Tip: Tell students that people often forget to read the labels on the sides and bottom of graphs. The side label gives the unit of measurement needed to answer the question.

Interpreting Information on Graphs

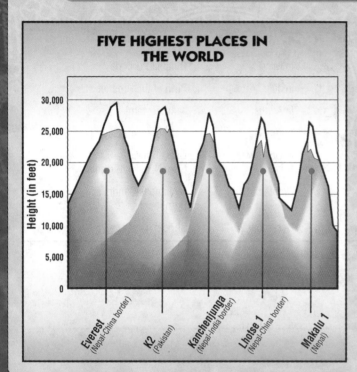

FIVE HIGHEST PLACES IN THE WORLD

Directions: Answer the following question based on the graph.

About how high is Mount Everest?

A 30,000 miles

B 30,000 meters

C 30,000 yards

D 30,000 feet

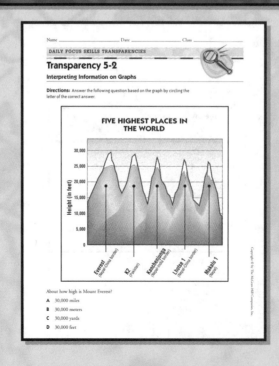

Name _____ Date _____ Class _____

DAILY FOCUS SKILLS TRANSPARENCIES

Transparency 5-2

Interpreting Information on Graphs

Directions: Answer the following question based on the graph by circling the letter of the correct answer.

FIVE HIGHEST PLACES IN THE WORLD

About how high is Mount Everest?

A   30,000 miles

B   30,000 meters

C   30,000 yards

D   30,000 feet

14

Unit 3

Section 6-1

UNIT 3 | **DAILY FOCUS SKILLS**
Chapter 6 | **TRANSPARENCY 6-1**

ANSWER: Students should recognize that large farm machinery cannot be used on these terraced fields. These fields are still worked by hand.
Teacher Tip: Have students imagine that they are standing in one of these fields.

Evaluating Visual Sources of Information

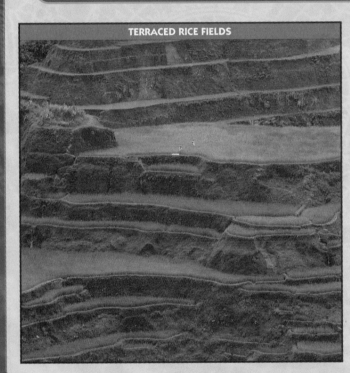

TERRACED RICE FIELDS

Directions: Answer the following question based on the photograph.

What effect do you think modern farming machinery has had on the laborers who work these rice fields?

_____

_____

_____

_____

Name _____ Date _____ Class _____

DAILY FOCUS SKILLS TRANSPARENCIES

Transparency 6-1

Evaluating Visual Sources of Information

Directions: Answer the following question based on the photograph in the space provided.

TERRACED RICE FIELDS

What effect do you think modern farming machinery has had on the laborers who work these rice fields?

Unit 3

Section 6-2

UNIT 3 | **DAILY FOCUS SKILLS**
Chapter 6 | **TRANSPARENCY 6-2**

ANSWER: If you have a friend who has a value system that is not equal to yours, you should not continue to be friends with that person.
Teacher Tip: Ask students why they agree or disagree with Kongfuzi's point of view.

Identifying Points of View

Quotations from Kongfuzi, a Chinese Philosopher

"When you have faults, do not fear to abandon them."

"Have no friends not equal to yourself."

Directions: Answer the following question based on the quotations.

What do you think the philosopher meant by the second quotation?

_____

_____

_____

_____

Name _____ Date _____ Class _____

DAILY FOCUS SKILLS TRANSPARENCIES

Transparency 6-2

Identifying Points of View

Directions: Answer the following question based on the quotations in the space provided.

Quotations from Kongfuzi, a Chinese Philosopher

"When you have faults, do not fear to abandon them."

"Have no friends not equal to yourself."

What do you think the philosopher meant by the second quotation?

_____

_____

_____

Unit 3

UNIT 3 | **DAILY FOCUS SKILLS**
Chapter 6 | **TRANSPARENCY 6-3**

ANSWER: United States; because U.S. consumers demand Taiwan's high-technology products.
Teacher Tip: Students should not only read the graph, they should draw on information from the text about Taiwan's products.

Interpreting Circle Graphs

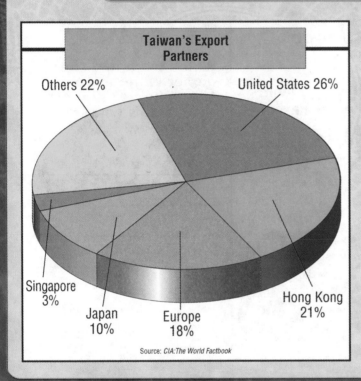

Taiwan's Export Partners

Others 22%
United States 26%
Singapore 3%
Japan 10%
Europe 18%
Hong Kong 21%

Source: *CIA:The World Factbook*

Directions: Answer the following question based on the graph.

Which country buys most of Taiwan's products? Why do you think this is so?

_____

_____

_____

_____

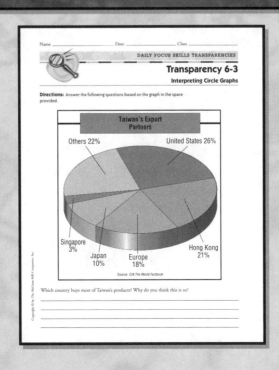

Name _____ Date _____ Class _____

DAILY FOCUS SKILLS TRANSPARENCIES

Transparency 6-3
Interpreting Circle Graphs

Directions: Answer the following questions based on the graph in the space provided.

Taiwan's Export Partners

Others 22%
United States 26%
Singapore 3%
Japan 10%
Europe 18%
Hong Kong 21%

Source: *CIA:The World Factbook*

Which country buys most of Taiwan's products? Why do you think this is so?

_____

_____

_____

Unit 3

Section 7-1

UNIT 3 | **DAILY FOCUS SKILLS**
Chapter 7 | **TRANSPARENCY 7-1**

ANSWER: The Fukuoka Daiei Hawks had the higher home winning percentage. It was 63 percent.

Teacher Tip: To find the percentages, divide the number of games won by the number of games played.

Analyzing Statistics

Japanese Baseball 2000 Season Results

Pacific League Champs Fukuoka Daiei Hawks

73 Wins
50 Losses, 2 Ties
Home: 43W, 25L
Road: 30W, 25L, 2T

Central League Champs Yomiuri Giants

78 Wins
57 Losses
Home: 38W, 29L
Road: 40W, 28L

Directions: Answer the following question based on the statistics.

Which team had the higher winning percentage at home? What was that team's winning percentage?

_____

_____

_____

_____

Name _____ Date _____ Class _____

DAILY FOCUS SKILLS TRANSPARENCIES

Transparency 7-1

Analyzing Statistics

Directions: Answer the following questions based on the statistics in the space provided.

Japanese Baseball 2000 Season Results

Pacific League Champs Fukuoka Daiei Hawks

73 Wins
50 Losses, 2 Ties
Home: 43W, 25L
Road: 30W, 25L, 2T

Central League Champs Yomiuri Giants

78 Wins
57 Losses
Home: 38W, 29L
Road: 40W, 28L

Which team had the higher winning percentage at home? What was that team's winning percentage?

_____

_____

_____

Unit 3

UNIT 3 | **DAILY FOCUS SKILLS**
Chapter 7 | **TRANSPARENCY 7-2**

ANSWER: 2–3 months

Teacher Tip: Remind students that time lines show the sequence of events. Students should use the title of the time line to identify the type of events shown on the time line.

Interpreting Information on Time Lines

Events of the Korean War

June 1950	North Korea attacks South Korea.
June 1950	President Harry Truman commits U.S. forces to assist South Korea.
July 1950	United Nations command formed to fight for South Korea.
September 1950	UN forces land in Inchon, South Korea.
November 1950	Troops from China cross into North Korea to fight against the UN.
January 1951	Seoul, South Korea, falls to North Korea.
March 1951	Seoul retaken by UN troops.
July 1953	Final cease-fire ends the war.
August 1953	Sides begin to exchange prisoners of war.

Directions: Answer the following question based on the time line.

For how long was Seoul, South Korea, under the control of North Korea?

_____

_____

_____

_____

Name _____ Date _____ Class _____

DAILY FOCUS SKILLS TRANSPARENCIES

Transparency 7-2

Interpreting Information on Time Lines

Directions: Answer the following question based on the time line in the space provided.

Events of the Korean War

June 1950	North Korea attacks South Korea.
June 1950	President Harry Truman commits U.S. forces to assist South Korea.
July 1950	United Nations command formed to fight for South Korea.
September 1950	UN forces land in Inchon, South Korea.
November 1950	Troops from China cross into North Korea to fight against the UN.
January 1951	Seoul, South Korea, falls to North Korea.
March 1951	Seoul retaken by UN troops.
July 1953	Final cease-fire ends the war.
August 1953	Sides begin to exchange prisoners of war.

For how long was Seoul, South Korea, under the control of North Korea?

Unit 3

UNIT 3 | **DAILY FOCUS SKILLS**
Chapter 8 | **TRANSPARENCY 8-1**

ANSWER: D

Teacher Tip: Tell students to read the choices carefully and eliminate any that are obviously false. Then have them compare the remaining choices to the reasons listed to identify the true statement.

Drawing Conclusions

Teakwood, a Popular Wood for Shipbuilding and Furniture Making

Resists Insects

Durable

Resists Decay

Easily Worked

Repels Water

Directions: Answer the following question based on the diagram.

From the information given, which of the following statements is true?

A Teakwood furniture will rot quickly if left in damp surroundings.

B A teakwood floor becomes slippery when wet.

C Termites quickly destroy furniture made of teakwood.

D Teakwood furniture can be used outdoors.

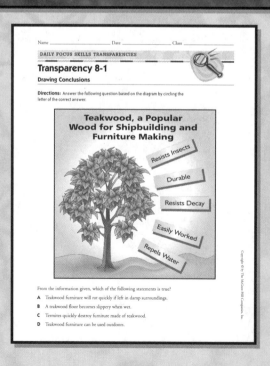

Name _____ Date _____ Class _____

DAILY FOCUS SKILLS TRANSPARENCIES

Transparency 8-1

Drawing Conclusions

Directions: Answer the following question based on the diagram by circling the letter of the correct answer.

Teakwood, a Popular Wood for Shipbuilding and Furniture Making

Resists Insects

Durable

Resists Decay

Easily Worked

Repels Water

From the information given, which of the following statements is true?

A Teakwood furniture will rot quickly if left in damp surroundings.

B A teakwood floor becomes slippery when wet.

C Termites quickly destroy furniture made of teakwood.

D Teakwood furniture can be used outdoors.

Unit 3

Section 8-2

UNIT 3 | **DAILY FOCUS SKILLS**
Chapter 8 | **TRANSPARENCY 8-2**

ANSWER: B

Teacher Tip: Encourage students to study the labels on the diagram carefully to identify the different parts of a volcano.

Interpreting Diagrams

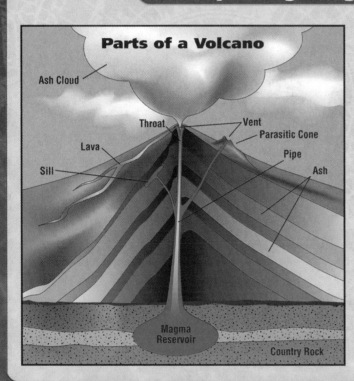

Parts of a Volcano

- Ash Cloud
- Throat
- Vent
- Parasitic Cone
- Lava
- Pipe
- Sill
- Ash
- Magma Reservoir
- Country Rock

Directions: Answer the following question based on the diagram.

Through what channel does the magma flow from inside the earth to the earth's crust?

A the sill

B the pipe

C the vent

D the cone

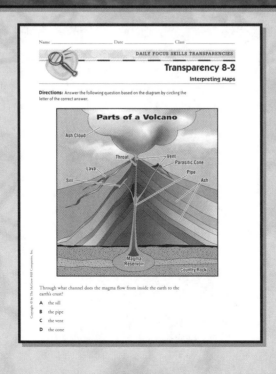

Name _____ Date _____ Class _____

DAILY FOCUS SKILLS TRANSPARENCIES

Transparency 8-2

Interpreting Maps

Directions: Answer the following question based on the diagram by circling the letter of the correct answer.

Parts of a Volcano

- Ash Cloud
- Throat
- Vent
- Parasitic Cone
- Lava
- Pipe
- Sill
- Ash
- Magma Reservoir
- Country Rock

Through what channel does the magma flow from inside the earth to the earth's crust?

A the sill

B the pipe

C the vent

D the cone

Unit 4

UNIT 4 | **DAILY FOCUS SKILLS**
Chapter 9 | **TRANSPARENCY 9-1**

ANSWER: A

Teacher Tip: Explain to students that comparing means identifying things that are similar, while contrasting means identifying the differences between two or more items.

Comparing and Contrasting

Greek Architecture

Doric   Ionic   Corinthian

Directions: Answer the following question based on the graphic.

Which of the column types is the most decorated?

A Corinthian

B Doric

C Ionic

D All are equally decorated.

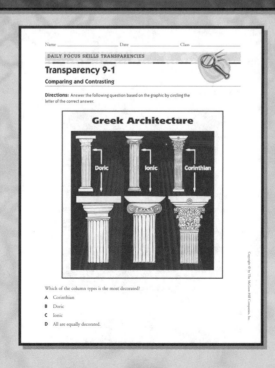

Name _____ Date _____ Class _____

DAILY FOCUS SKILLS TRANSPARENCIES

Transparency 9-1

Comparing and Contrasting

Directions: Answer the following question based on the graphic by circling the letter of the correct answer.

Greek Architecture

Doric   Ionic   Corinthian

Which of the column types is the most decorated?

A Corinthian

B Doric

C Ionic

D All are equally decorated.

Unit 4

UNIT 4 | **DAILY FOCUS SKILLS**
Chapter 9 | **TRANSPARENCY 9-2**

ANSWER: D

Teacher Tip: Taller and thinner walls meant more glass could be included in the windows, making large stained glass windows possible.

Interpreting Diagrams

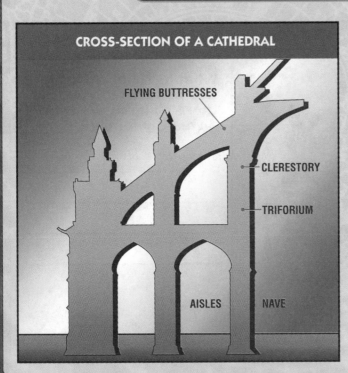

CROSS-SECTION OF A CATHEDRAL

FLYING BUTTRESSES

CLERESTORY

TRIFORIUM

AISLES   NAVE

Directions: Answer the following question based on the graphic.

Which architectural feature allowed for taller walls?

A Clerestory

B Triforium

C Aisles

D Flying buttresses

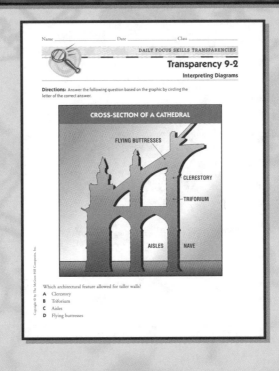

Name _____ Date _____ Class _____

DAILY FOCUS SKILLS TRANSPARENCIES

Transparency 9-2

Interpreting Diagrams

Directions: Answer the following question based on the graphic by circling the letter of the correct answer.

CROSS-SECTION OF A CATHEDRAL

FLYING BUTTRESSES

CLERESTORY

TRIFORIUM

AISLES   NAVE

Which architectural feature allowed for taller walls?
A Clerestory
B Triforium
C Aisles
D Flying buttresses

Unit 4

UNIT 4 | **DAILY FOCUS SKILLS**
Chapter 9 | **TRANSPARENCY 9-3**

ANSWER: Items include jewelry and expensive fabrics. Only wealthy families made portraits of their children.

Teacher Tip: Other women artists of the period include Artemesia Gentileschi and Lavinia Fontana.

Interpreting Art

SOFONISBA ANGUISSOLA (1532-1625)

Sofonisba Anguissola was one of the few women painters to gain an international reputation. Painters such as Michelangelo, Vasari, and Van Dyck were familiar with her work. She specialized in portraits of royalty and royal court families.

Directions: Answer the following question based on the information provided.

What kinds of things in this picture tell you that these children are from a wealthy family?

_____

_____

_____

_____

Name _____ Date _____ Class _____

DAILY FOCUS SKILLS TRANSPARENCIES

Transparency 9-3

Interpreting Art

Directions: Answer the following question based on the information provided in the space provided.

SOFONISBA ANGUISSOLA (1532–1625)

Sofonisba Anguissola was one of the few women painters to gain an international reputation. Painters such as Michelangelo, Vasari, and Van Dyck were familiar with her work. She specialized in portraits of royalty and royal court families.

What kinds of things in this picture tell you that these children are from a wealthy family?

_____
_____
_____

24

Unit 4

Section 10-1

UNIT 4 | **DAILY FOCUS SKILLS**
Chapter 10 | **TRANSPARENCY 10-1**

ANSWER: A

Teacher Tip: The potato famine of the 1840s and 1850s increased immigration to the United States from Ireland.

Interpreting Bar Graphs

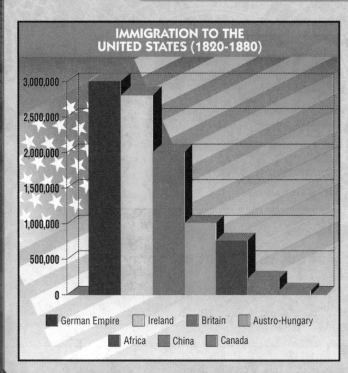

**IMMIGRATION TO THE
UNITED STATES (1820-1880)**

Directions: Answer the following question based on the graphic.

Where did the most immigrants come from during this period?

A German Empire

B Africa

C Austro-Hungarian Empire

D Canada

- German Empire
- Ireland
- Britain
- Austro-Hungary
- Africa
- China
- Canada

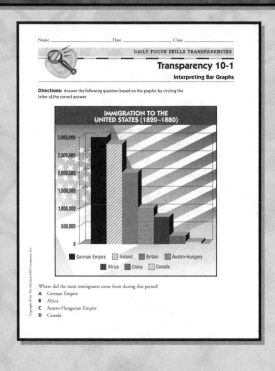

Name _____ Date _____ Class _____

DAILY FOCUS SKILLS TRANSPARENCIES

Transparency 10-1

Interpreting Bar Graphs

Directions: Answer the following question based on the graphic by circling the letter of the correct answer.

**IMMIGRATION TO THE
UNITED STATES (1820–1880)**

- German Empire
- Ireland
- Britain
- Austro-Hungary
- Africa
- China
- Canada

Where did the most immigrants come from during this period?
A German Empire
B Africa
C Austro-Hungarian Empire
D Canada

Unit 4

UNIT 4 | **DAILY FOCUS SKILLS**
Chapter 10 | **TRANSPARENCY 10-2**

ANSWER: It implies that the Soviet government had built up its military, ignoring its citizens' basic economic needs.

Teacher Tip: Explain that during the Cold War the United States and the Soviet Union built up their militaries.

Interpreting Social and Political Messages of Cartoons

"AT THIS POINT THE ARTIST RAN OUT OF PAINT."

© 1980 Ranan R. Lurie

Directions: Answer the following question based on the cartoon.

What does this cartoon imply about the Soviet economy during the Cold War?

_____

_____

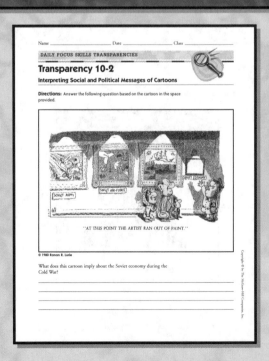

Unit 4

Section 10-3

UNIT 4 | **DAILY FOCUS SKILLS**
Chapter 10 | **TRANSPARENCY 10-3**

ANSWER: C

Teacher Tip: This question asks for the years in which the difference between exports and imports has been the greatest. This will be the point at which the two lines are farthest apart.

Analyzing Statistics

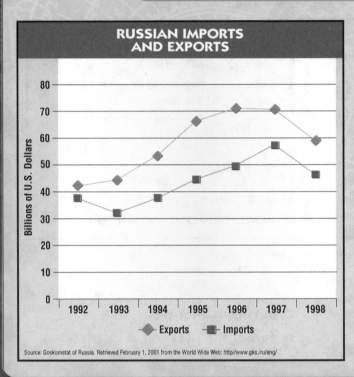

RUSSIAN IMPORTS AND EXPORTS

Directions: Answer the following question based on the graphic.

In what years has the difference between Russian exports and imports been the greatest?

A 1992 and 1998

B 1992 and 1993

C 1995 and 1996

D 1996 and 1997

Source: Goskomstat of Russia. Retrieved February 1, 2001 from the World Wide Web: http://www.gks./ru/eng/

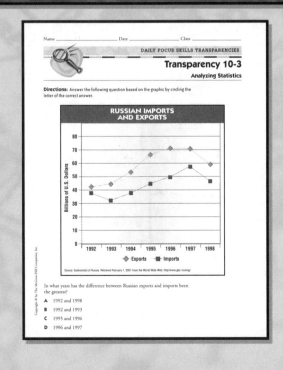

Name _____ Date _____ Class _____

DAILY FOCUS SKILLS TRANSPARENCIES

Transparency 10-3
Analyzing Statistics

Directions: Answer the following question based on the graphic by circling the letter of the correct answer.

RUSSIAN IMPORTS AND EXPORTS

In what years has the difference between Russian exports and imports been the greatest?

A 1992 and 1998

B 1992 and 1993

C 1995 and 1996

D 1996 and 1997

Source: Goskomstat of Russia. Retrieved February 1, 2001 from the World Wide Web: http://www.gks./ru/eng/

Unit 4

Section 11-1

UNIT 4
Chapter 11

DAILY FOCUS SKILLS
TRANSPARENCY 11-1

ANSWER: B

Teacher Tip: Tell students that *Auld Lang Syne* is a poem that has been set to music and is traditionally sung on New Year's Eve.

Using Primary Sources

AULD LANG SYNE
By Robert Burns, Scottish poet, 1788

Should auld acquaintance be forgot,
And never brought to mind?
Should auld acquaintance be forgot,
And auld lang syne?

For auld lang syne, my jo,
For auld lang syne,
We'll tak a cup o' kindness yet
For auld lang syne.

DAYS LONG AGO
Modern English Translation

Should old acquaintances be forgotten
And never be remembered?
Should old acquaintances be forgotten
and days of long ago?

For days long ago, my dear,
For days long ago
We'll drink a cup of kindness yet
For days long ago!

Directions: Answer the following question based on the information above.

What does Auld Lang Syne mean?

A old, long signs

C old acquaintances

B days long ago

D forget the past

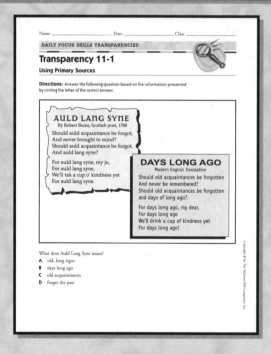

28

Unit 4

Section 11-2

UNIT 4 | **DAILY FOCUS SKILLS**
Chapter 11 | **TRANSPARENCY 11-2**

ANSWER: Take the B Line and transfer to the C Line.

Teacher Tip: Tell students that a subway is an under-ground transportation system that uses trains to move people quickly from place to place.

Interpreting Maps

Paris Subway Map

Directions: Answer the following question based on the map.

Describe a route from Charles de Gaulle Airport to Orly Airport.

_____

_____

_____

_____

Name _____ Date _____ Class _____

DAILY FOCUS SKILLS TRANSPARENCIES

Transparency 11-2

Interpreting Maps

Directions: Answer the following question based on the map in the space provided.

Paris Subway Map

Describe a route from Charles de Gaulle Airport to Orly Airport.

_____
_____
_____

Unit 4

UNIT 4 | **DAILY FOCUS SKILLS**
Chapter 11 | **TRANSPARENCY 11-3**

ANSWER: A

Teacher Tip: Tell students that column titles describe the type of information found in the column.

Interpreting Charts

FAMOUS COMPOSERS AND THEIR MUSIC			
Austrian Composers	German Composers	Type of Music Composed	Performed by
Franz Schubert	Johann Sebastian Bach Ludwig van Beethoven	Chamber Music	small groups with each member playing a different instrument
Franz Joseph Haydn	Johann Sebastian Bach George Frideric Handel	Concertos	larger groups with multiple instruments and one featured instrument
Franz Joseph Haydn Franz Schubert Wolfgang Amadeus Mozart	Ludwig van Beethoven	Symphonies	long musical works performed by an orchestra

Directions: Answer the following question based on the chart.

Which Austrian composer wrote both chamber music and symphonies?

A Franz Schubert

B Franz Joseph Haydn

C Ludwig van Beethoven

D Wolfgang Amadeus Mozart

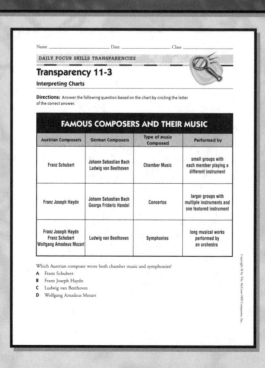

Name _____ Date _____ Class _____

DAILY FOCUS SKILLS TRANSPARENCIES

Transparency 11-3
Interpreting Charts

Directions: Answer the following question based on the chart by circling the letter of the correct answer.

FAMOUS COMPOSERS AND THEIR MUSIC			
Austrian Composers	German Composers	Type of Music Composed	Performed by
Franz Schubert	Johann Sebastian Bach Ludwig van Beethoven	Chamber Music	small groups with each member playing a different instrument
Franz Joseph Haydn	Johann Sebastian Bach George Frideric Handel	Concertos	larger groups with multiple instruments and one featured instrument
Franz Joseph Haydn Franz Schubert Wolfgang Amadeus Mozart	Ludwig van Beethoven	Symphonies	long musical works performed by an orchestra

Which Austrian composer wrote both chamber music and symphonies?

A   Franz Schubert
B   Franz Joseph Haydn
C   Ludwig van Beethoven
D   Wolfgang Amadeus Mozart

Unit 4

Section 11-4

UNIT 4 | **DAILY FOCUS SKILLS**
Chapter 11 | **TRANSPARENCY 11-4**

ANSWER: C

Teacher Tip: Use the model to explain the process that causes water and steam to spew from a geyser.

Organizing and Interpreting Diagrams

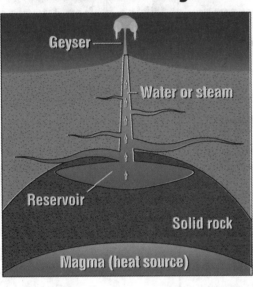

Model of a Geyser

Geyser

Water or steam

Reservoir

Solid rock

Magma (heat source)

Directions: Answer the following question based on the diagram.

What provides the heat source for the water that erupts as a geyser?

A solid rocks below the earth's surface

B steam

C magma

D reservoir

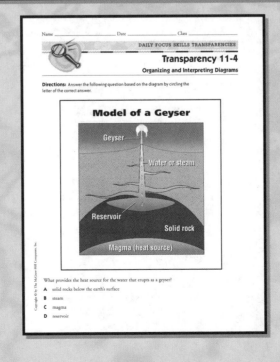

Name _____ Date _____ Class _____

DAILY FOCUS SKILLS TRANSPARENCIES

Transparency 11-4
Organizing and Interpreting Diagrams

Directions: Answer the following question based on the diagram by circling the letter of the correct answer.

Model of a Geyser

Geyser

Water or steam

Reservoir

Solid rock

Magma (heat source)

Copyright © by The McGraw-Hill Companies, Inc.

What provides the heat source for the water that erupts as a geyser?

A solid rocks below the earth's surface

B steam

C magma

D reservoir

Unit 4

Section 11-5

UNIT 4 | **DAILY FOCUS SKILLS**
Chapter 11 | **TRANSPARENCY 11-5**

ANSWER: A

Teacher Tip: Tell students that we often identify places with something that is famous or unique to the place. Ask students to identify why they think each item is associated with its city.

Interpreting Diagrams

Directions: Answer the following question based on the images.

Which Italian city do you think is well-known for its art treasures?

A Florence

B Pisa

C Rome

D Venice

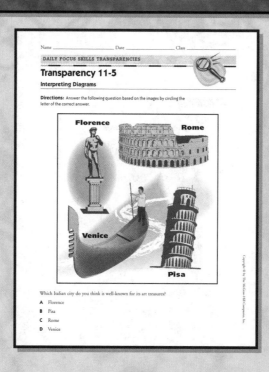

Name _____ Date _____ Class _____

DAILY FOCUS SKILLS TRANSPARENCIES

Transparency 11-5

Interpreting Diagrams

Directions: Answer the following question based on the images by circling the letter of the correct answer.

Which Italian city do you think is well-known for its art treasures?

A Florence

B Pisa

C Rome

D Venice

Unit 4

UNIT 4 | **DAILY FOCUS SKILLS**
Chapter 12 | **TRANSPARENCY 12-1**

ANSWER: D

Teacher Tip: Tell students to use the process of elimination to sort through the answer choices. Explain to students that a common language can help create a national identity.

Interpreting Maps

LANGUAGES OF THE BALTIC REPUBLICS

Finland

Gulf of Finland

Baltic Sea

Estonia:
Estonian, Russian, Ukrainian, English, Finnish

Russia

Latvia:
Latvian, Lithuanian, Russian

Lithuania:
Lithuanian, Polish, Russian

Belarus

Poland

Directions: Answer the following question based on the map.

Which language is spoken in all three Baltic republics?

A English

B Estonian

C Lithuanian

D Russian

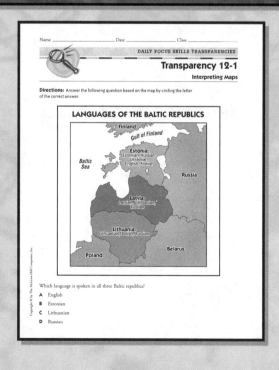

Name _____ Date _____ Class _____

DAILY FOCUS SKILLS TRANSPARENCIES

Transparency 12-1
Interpreting Maps

Directions: Answer the following question based on the map by circling the letter of the correct answer.

LANGUAGES OF THE BALTIC REPUBLICS

Finland

Gulf of Finland

Baltic Sea

Estonia: Estonian, Russian, Ukrainian, English, Finnish

Russia

Latvia: Latvian, Lithuanian, Russian

Lithuania: Lithuanian, Polish, Russian

Belarus

Poland

Which language is spoken in all three Baltic republics?
A English
B Estonian
C Lithuanian
D Russian

Copyright © by The McGraw-Hill Companies, Inc.

Section 12-2

UNIT 4 | **DAILY FOCUS SKILLS**
Chapter 12 | **TRANSPARENCY 12-2**

ANSWER: B

Teacher Tip: Remind students that countries are shown in the columns (vertically) and ethnic groups in the rows (horizontally).

Interpreting Information on Charts

ETHNIC GROUPS IN SELECTED COUNTRIES							
ETHNIC GROUP	ALBANIA	BOSNIA & HERZEGOVINA	BULGARIA	CROATIA	MACEDONIA (F.Y.R.O.M.)	ROMANIA	SLOVENIA	YUGOSLAVIA (SERBIA & MONTENEGRO)
Albanian	95%			0.3%	22.7%			16.5%
Bosnian		44%					1%	
Bulgarian			83%					
Croatian		17%		78.1%			3%	
Greek	3%							
Hungarian				0.5%		7.1%		3.3%
Macedonian					66.6%			
Montenegrin				0.3%				5.0%
Muslim				0.9%			1%	
Romanian						89.5%		
Serbian		31%		12.2%	2.1%		2%	62.6%
Slovene				0.5%			88%	
Turk			9%		4.0%			
Other	2%	8%	8%	8.2%	4.6%	3.4%	5%	12.6%

Directions: Answer the following question based on the chart.

Which country has the largest number of ethnic groups in its population?

A Bosnia and Herzegovina

C Slovenia

B Croatia

D Yugoslavia

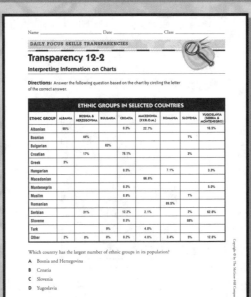

Unit 4

UNIT 4 | **DAILY FOCUS SKILLS**
Chapter 12 | **TRANSPARENCY 12-3**

ANSWER: You would need to know the land area.

Teacher Tip: To answer this question, have students recall how geographers calculate population density, and substitute "train tracks" for "population."

Interpreting Diagrams

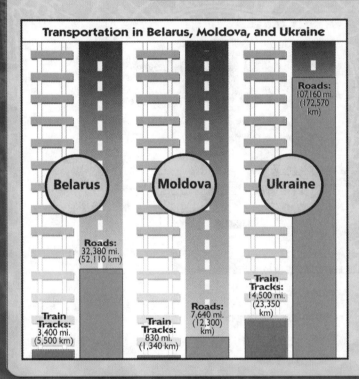

Transportation in Belarus, Moldova, and Ukraine

Belarus

Moldova

Ukraine

Roads: 107,160 mi. (172,570 km)

Roads: 32,380 mi. (52,110 km)

Roads: 7,640 mi. (12,300) km)

Train Tracks: 14,500 mi. (23,350 km)

Train Tracks: 3,400 mi. (5,500 km)

Train Tracks: 830 mi. (1,340 km)

Directions: Answer the following question based on the diagram.

To understand the density of train tracks in these countries, what other information would you need to know?

_____

_____

_____

_____

Name _____ Date _____ Class _____

DAILY FOCUS SKILLS TRANSPARENCIES

Transparency 12-3

Interpreting Diagrams

Directions: Answer the following question based on the diagram in the space provided.

Transportation in Belarus, Moldova, and Ukraine

Belarus

Moldova

Ukraine

Roads: 107,160 mi. (172,570 km)

Roads: 32,380 mi. (52,110 km)

Roads: 7,640 mi. (12,300) km)

Train Tracks: 14,500 mi. (23,350 km)

Train Tracks: 3,400 mi. (5,500 km)

Train Tracks: 830 mi. (1,340 km)

To understand the density of train tracks in these countries, what other information would you need to know?

Copyright © by The McGraw-Hill Companies, Inc.

Unit 5

UNIT 5 | **DAILY FOCUS SKILLS**
Chapter 13 | **TRANSPARENCY 13-1**

ANSWER: B

Teacher Tip: If students are having trouble identifying countries, have them compare this map to a world map with countries labeled in their textbook.

Interpreting Maps

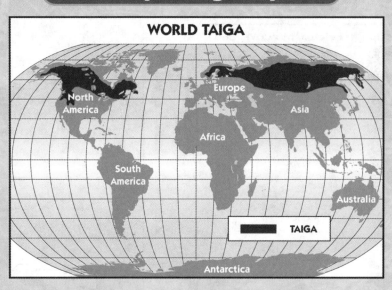

WORLD TAIGA

■ **TAIGA**

Directions: Answer the following question based on the map.

Most of the taiga is located in which two countries?

A Russia and the United States

C the United States and Canada

B Russia and Canada

D Russia and China

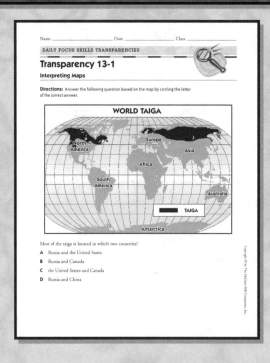

36

Unit 5

Section 13-2

UNIT 5 | **DAILY FOCUS SKILLS**
Chapter 13 | **TRANSPARENCY 13-2**

ANSWER: During the Soviet era the government tried to suppress religion.

Teacher Tip: Peter the Great ordered that the celebration of New Year's be moved from March to January 1 to align with western European tradition.

Drawing Conclusions

FATHER FROST

The religious festival of the Feast of St. Nicholas was observed in Russia for centuries, and St. Nicholas was known as Father Christmas. After the Communist revolution, the celebration of the feast was prohibited. St. Nicholas was transformed into *Ded Moroz*, or Father Frost, the Russian Spirit of Winter, who brings gifts to children on New Year's Day. Russians also decorate *yolki*, pine or fir trees, for New Year's.

Directions: Answer the following question based on the reading.

Why do you think St. Nicholas became Father Frost under the Communist leadership in Russia?

_____

_____

_____

_____

Name _____ Date _____ Class _____

DAILY FOCUS SKILLS TRANSPARENCIES

Transparency 13-2
Drawing Conclusions

Directions: Answer the following question based on the reading in the space provided.

FATHER FROST

The religious festival of the Feast of St. Nicholas was observed in Russia for centuries, and St. Nicholas was known as Father Christmas. After the Communist revolution, the celebration of the feast was prohibited. St. Nicholas was transformed into *Ded Moroz*, or Father Frost, the Russian Spirit of Winter, who brings gifts to children on New Year's Day. Russians also decorate *yolki*, pine or fir trees, for New Year's.

Why do you think St. Nicholas became Father Frost under the Communist leadership in Russia?

_____

_____

Section 13-3

UNIT 5 | **DAILY FOCUS SKILLS**
Chapter 13 | **TRANSPARENCY 13-3**

ANSWER: A

Teacher Tip: Make sure that students understand that each segment of the bars represents a percentage of the total population of each country.

Interpreting Bar Graphs

MAJOR RELIGIONS OF THE CENTRAL ASIAN REPUBLICS

Country (y-axis): Uzbekistan, Turkmenistan, Tajikistan, Kyrgyzstan, Kazakhstan

Percentages (x-axis): 0, 20, 40, 60, 80, 100

Legend: Muslim | Russian or Eastern Orthodox | Protestant | Other/Unknown

Directions: Answer the following question based on the bar graph.

In which country do Muslims make up less than half the population?

A Kazakhstan

B Kyrgyzstan

C Tajikistan

D Turkmenistan

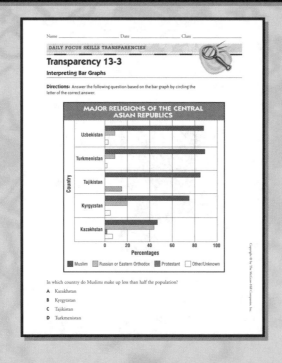

Name _____ Date _____ Class _____

DAILY FOCUS SKILLS TRANSPARENCIES

Transparency 13-3

Interpreting Bar Graphs

Directions: Answer the following question based on the bar graph by circling the letter of the correct answer.

MAJOR RELIGIONS OF THE CENTRAL ASIAN REPUBLICS

Country: Uzbekistan, Turkmenistan, Tajikistan, Kyrgyzstan, Kazakhstan

Percentages: 0, 20, 40, 60, 80, 100

Legend: Muslim | Russian or Eastern Orthodox | Protestant | Other/Unknown

In which country do Muslims make up less than half the population?

A Kazakhstan

B Kyrgyzstan

C Tajikistan

D Turkmenistan

Unit 5

Section 14-1

UNIT 5 | **DAILY FOCUS SKILLS**
Chapter 14 | **TRANSPARENCY 14-1**

ANSWER: A

Teacher Tip: Remind students that a country that is landlocked is completely surrounded by land, and does not border any bodies of water.

Interpreting Maps

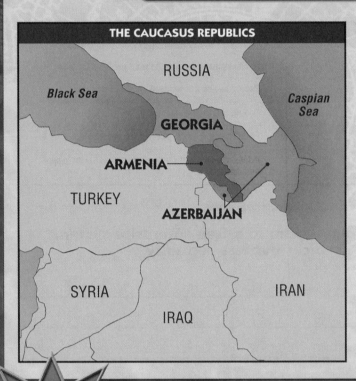

THE CAUCASUS REPUBLICS

RUSSIA
Black Sea
Caspian Sea
GEORGIA
ARMENIA
TURKEY
AZERBAIJAN
SYRIA
IRAQ
IRAN

Directions: Answer the following question based on the map.

Which Caucasus republic is landlocked?

A Armenia

B Azerbaijan

C Georgia

D Iran

This full-sized transparency is included in this Sampler!

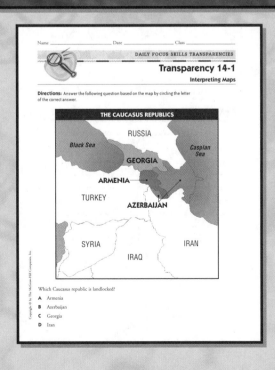

Name _____ Date _____ Class _____

DAILY FOCUS SKILLS TRANSPARENCIES

Transparency 14-1

Interpreting Maps

Directions: Answer the following question based on the map by circling the letter of the correct answer.

THE CAUCASUS REPUBLICS

RUSSIA
Black Sea
Caspian Sea
GEORGIA
ARMENIA
TURKEY
AZERBAIJAN
SYRIA
IRAQ
IRAN

Which Caucasus republic is landlocked?

A Armenia
B Azerbaijan
C Georgia
D Iran

Unit 5

Section 14-2

UNIT 5 | **DAILY FOCUS SKILLS**
Chapter 14 | **TRANSPARENCY 14-2**

ANSWER: People have more choices but may be unemployed and unable to afford goods.

Teacher Tip: Explain to students that freedom to choose can have positive and negative consequences.

Comparing and Contrasting

COMMUNISM	FREE ENTERPRISE SYSTEM
Government decides what products to make.	Business managers decide what products to make.
All people have jobs.	People can be unemployed.
People work in assigned jobs.	People can choose their jobs.
Limited goods and services available.	Wide choice of goods and services available.
Prices of goods and services kept low.	Prices of goods and services rise and fall with supply and demand.

Directions: Answer the following question based on the information given.

How has the move from communism to a free enterprise system given Russian people more choices but less certainty?

_____

_____

_____

Name _____ Date _____ Class _____

DAILY FOCUS SKILLS TRANSPARENCIES

Transparency 14-2
Comparing and Contrasting

Directions: Answer the following question based on the information given in the space provided.

COMMUNISM	FREE ENTERPRISE SYSTEM
Government decides what products to make.	Business managers decide what products to make.
All people have jobs.	People can be unemployed.
People work in assigned jobs.	People can choose their jobs.
Limited goods and services available.	Wide choice of goods and services available.
Prices of goods and services kept low.	Prices of goods and services rise and fall with supply and demand.

How has the move from communism to a free enterprise system given
Russian people more choices but less certainty?

_____

_____

_____

Unit 6

UNIT 6 | **DAILY FOCUS SKILLS**
Chapter 15 | **TRANSPARENCY 15-1**

ANSWER: They will likely become extinct.

Teacher Tip: Tell students that predictions are more than guesses. Predictions are based on observing past events and experiences.

Making Predictions

Some of the Endangered Mammals of Africa

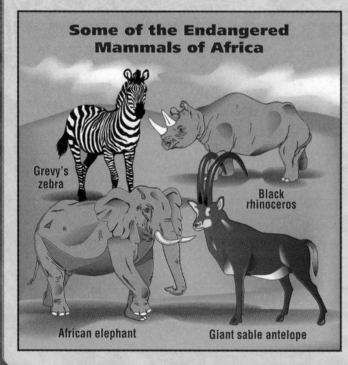

Grevy's zebra

Black rhinoceros

African elephant

Giant sable antelope

Directions: Answer the following question based on the information presented.

What do you think will happen to these endangered mammals if they continue to be hunted?

_____

_____

_____

_____

Name _____ Date _____ Class _____

DAILY FOCUS SKILLS TRANSPARENCIES

Transparency 15-1

Making Predictions

Directions: Answer the following question based on the information presented in the space provided.

Some of the Endangered Mammals of Africa

Grevy's zebra

Black rhinoceros

African elephant

Giant sable antelope

What do you think will happen to these endangered mammals if they continue to be hunted?

_____

_____

_____

Unit 6

Section 15-2

UNIT 6 | **DAILY FOCUS SKILLS**
Chapter 15 | **TRANSPARENCY 15-2**

ANSWER: Khartoum, Sudan, has a desert climate because of the small amount of rainfall it receives.

Teacher Tip: Ask students which information (temperature or rainfall) is more important in identifying a desert climate.

Interpreting Information on Tables

Addis Ababa, Ethiopia

Month	Jan.	Feb.	Mar.	Apr.	May	June	July	Aug.	Sept.	Oct.	Nov.	Dec.
Average Temperature*	61°	63°	65°	64°	65°	62°	60°	60°	61°	61°	60°	58°
Rainfall	0.7"	1.5"	2.7"	3.4"	3.4"	5.2"	10.5"	11.1"	7.3"	1.1"	0.4"	0.4"

Khartoum, Sudan

Month	Jan.	Feb.	Mar.	Apr.	May	June	July	Aug.	Sept.	Oct.	Nov.	Dec.
Average Temperature*	73°	75°	82°	88°	93°	93°	89°	87°	89°	89°	82°	75°
Rainfall	0"	0"	0"	0"	0.1"	0.3"	1.9"	2.7"	0.8"	0.2"	0"	0"

*Temperatures in Fahrenheit

Directions: Answer the following question based on the table.

Which city do you think has a desert climate? Why?

_____

_____

_____

Name _____ Date _____ Class _____

DAILY FOCUS SKILLS TRANSPARENCIES

Transparency 15-2

Interpreting Information on Tables

Directions: Answer the following question based on the table in the space provided.

Addis Ababa, Ethiopia

Month	Jan.	Feb.	Mar.	Apr.	May	June	July	Aug.	Sept.	Oct.	Nov.	Dec.
Average Temperature*	61°	63°	65°	64°	65°	62°	60°	60°	61°	61°	60°	58°
Rainfall	0.7"	1.5"	2.7"	3.4"	3.4"	5.2"	10.5"	11.1"	7.3"	1.1"	0.4"	0.4"

Khartoum, Sudan

Month	Jan.	Feb.	Mar.	Apr.	May	June	July	Aug.	Sept.	Oct.	Nov.	Dec.
Average Temperature*	73°	75°	82°	88°	93°	93°	89°	87°	89°	89°	82°	75°
Rainfall	0"	0"	0"	0"	0.1"	0.3"	1.9"	2.7"	0.8"	0.2"	0"	0"

*Temperatures in Fahrenheit

Which city do you think has a desert climate? Why?

_____

_____

Unit 6

Section 15-3

UNIT 6 | **DAILY FOCUS SKILLS**
Chapter 15 | **TRANSPARENCY 15-3**

ANSWER: Countries may change their flags when there is a major political change.

Teacher Tip: The Democratic Republic of the Congo changed its flag when it gained independence.

Interpreting Cause-and-Effect Relationships

Historic Flags of the Democratic Republic of the Congo

1885–1960

1963–1971

1960–1963

1971–Present

Directions: Answer the following question based on the images.

What do you think might cause a country to change its national flag?

_____

_____

_____

_____

Name _____ Date _____ Class _____

DAILY FOCUS SKILLS TRANSPARENCIES

Transparency 15-3

Interpreting Cause-and-Effect Relationships

Directions: Answer the following question based on the images in the space provided.

Historic Flags of the Democratic Republic of the Congo

1885–1960

1963–1971

1960–1963

1971–Present

What do you think might cause a country to change its national flag?

_____

_____

Unit 6

Section 16-1

UNIT 6 | **DAILY FOCUS SKILLS**
Chapter 16 | **TRANSPARENCY 16-1**

ANSWER: D

Teacher Tip: Ask students to carefully read the map and map key before answering the question. Remind students that ethnic groups share a common language, culture, or history.

Interpreting Maps

MAJOR NIGERIAN ETHNIC GROUPS

Directions: Answer the following question based on the map.

Which ethnic group lives the farthest north in Nigeria?

A Ekoi

B Ijaw

C Hausa

D Kanduri

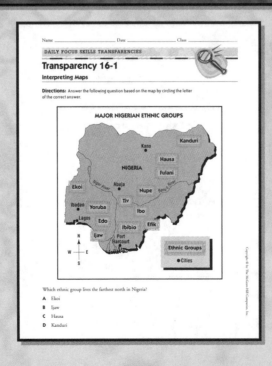

Name _____ Date _____ Class _____

DAILY FOCUS SKILLS TRANSPARENCIES

Transparency 16-1

Interpreting Maps

Directions: Answer the following question based on the map by circling the letter of the correct answer.

MAJOR NIGERIAN ETHNIC GROUPS

Which ethnic group lives the farthest north in Nigeria?

A   Ekoi

B   Ijaw

C   Hausa

D   Kanduri

Unit 6

UNIT 6 | **DAILY FOCUS SKILLS**
Chapter 16 | **TRANSPARENCY 16-2**

ANSWER: D

Teacher Tip: Tell students that time lines show the order of events and indicate the length of events.

Interpreting Information on Time Lines

Major Periods in Sahel History

- **African Empires** (A.D. 500s – late 1500s)
  - **Ghana Empire:** 500s – 1203
  - **Mali Empire:** 1203 – 1471
  - **Songhai Empire:** 1471 – 1591
- **Moroccan invasion:** 1591
- **Period of small states:** 1591 – 1880s
- **French rule:** 1880s – 1960s
- **Independence:** 1960s

Directions: Answer the following question based on the time line.

What was the last of the African empires to decline?

A Ghana

B Mali

C Moroccan

D Songhai

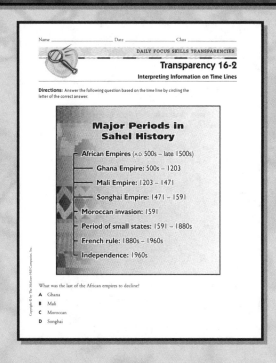

Name _____ Date _____ Class _____

DAILY FOCUS SKILLS TRANSPARENCIES

Transparency 16-2
Interpreting Information on Time Lines

Directions: Answer the following question based on the time line by circling the letter of the correct answer.

Major Periods in Sahel History

- African Empires (A.D. 500s – late 1500s)
  - Ghana Empire: 500s – 1203
  - Mali Empire: 1203 – 1471
  - Songhai Empire: 1471 – 1591
- Moroccan invasion: 1591
- Period of small states: 1591 – 1880s
- French rule: 1880s – 1960s
- Independence: 1960s

What was the last of the African empires to decline?

A Ghana

B Mali

C Moroccan

D Songhai

Unit 6

Section 17-1

UNIT 6 | **DAILY FOCUS SKILLS**
Chapter 17 | **TRANSPARENCY 17-1**

ANSWER: B

Teacher Tip: Tell students that one way to analyze statistics is to count the number of items or groups.

Analyzing Statistics

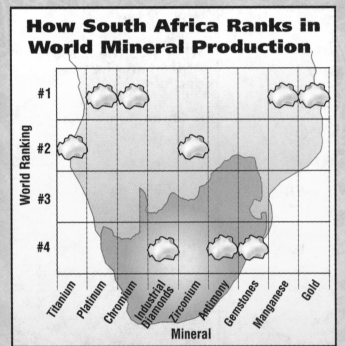

How South Africa Ranks in World Mineral Production

Directions: Answer the following question based on the diagram.

For how many of the minerals does South Africa rank number one in world production?

A three

B four

C six

D nine

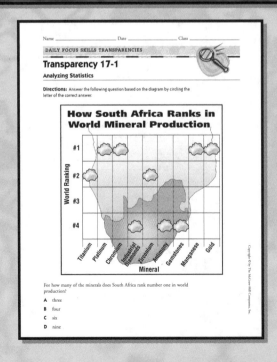

Name _____ Date _____ Class _____

DAILY FOCUS SKILLS TRANSPARENCIES

Transparency 17-1

Analyzing Statistics

Directions: Answer the following question based on the diagram by circling the letter of the correct answer.

How South Africa Ranks in World Mineral Production

For how many of the minerals does South Africa rank number one in world production?

A three

B four

C six

D nine

Unit 6

Section 17-2

Copyright © by The McGraw-Hill Companies, Inc.

UNIT 6 **DAILY FOCUS SKILLS**
Chapter 17 **TRANSPARENCY 17-2**

ANSWER: A

Teacher Tip: Remind students to read the question carefully and identify the key word or words. The key word in this question is *least*.

Interpreting Bar Graphs

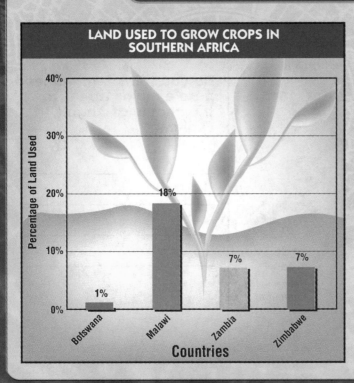

LAND USED TO GROW CROPS IN SOUTHERN AFRICA

Directions: Answer the following question based on the bar graph.

Which country has the least amount of land that is used to grow crops?

A Botswana

B Malawi

C Zambia

D Zimbabwe

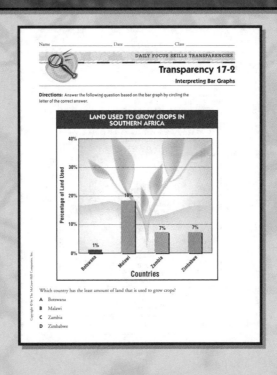

Unit 6

Section 17-3

UNIT 6 | **DAILY FOCUS SKILLS**
Chapter 17 | **TRANSPARENCY 17-3**

Supporting a Point of View

Land Mines in Angola

"UNITA [one side in the Angolan civil war] has also used land mines to control and effectively imprison populations under its control by planting mines around villages."

–Land Mine Monitor Report 2000
International Campaign to Ban Land Mines (ICBL)

Number of amputees from land mine accidents: 70,000

Population of Angola: 12,479,000

Estimated number of land mines: 10 to 20 million

Directions: Answer the following question based on the information presented.

Do you think land mines pose a major threat to the people of Angola? Explain.

_____

_____

_____

_____

Name _____ Date _____ Class _____

DAILY FOCUS SKILLS TRANSPARENCIES

Transparency 17-3

Supporting a Point of View

Directions: Answer the following question based on the information presented in the space provided.

Land Mines in Angola

"UNITA [one side in the Angolan civil war] has also used land mines to control and effectively imprison populations under its control by planting mines around villages."

–Land Mine Monitor Report 2000
International Campaign to Ban Land Mines (ICBL)

Number of amputees from land mine accidents: 70,000

Population of Angola: 12,479,000

Estimated number of land mines: 10 to 20 million

Do you think land mines pose a major threat to the people of Angola? Explain.

_____

_____

_____

Unit 7

Section 18-1

UNIT 7 | **DAILY FOCUS SKILLS**
Chapter 18 | **TRANSPARENCY 18-1**

ANSWER: D

Teacher Tip: Remind students that the title of the graph explains the type of data that is represented in the graph. In this case, the title explains that the number of lakes in Canada is shown by economic region.

Interpreting Bar Graphs

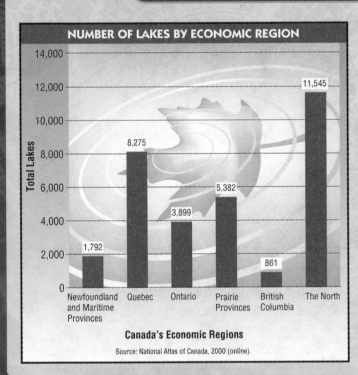

NUMBER OF LAKES BY ECONOMIC REGION

Total Lakes

14,000
12,000 — 11,545
10,000
8,000 — 8,275
6,000 — 5,382
4,000 — 3,899
2,000 — 1,792 / 861
0

Newfoundland and Maritime Provinces / Quebec / Ontario / Prairie Provinces / British Columbia / The North

Canada's Economic Regions

Source: National Atlas of Canada, 2000 (online).

Directions: Answer the following question based on the bar graph.

Which economic region of Canada has the most lakes?

A Newfoundland and Maritime Provinces

B Quebec

C Prairie Provinces

D The North

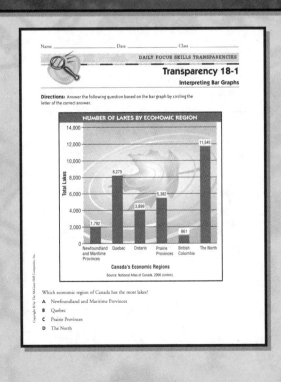

Name _____ Date _____ Class _____

DAILY FOCUS SKILLS TRANSPARENCIES

Transparency 18-1

Interpreting Bar Graphs

Directions: Answer the following question based on the bar graph by circling the letter of the correct answer.

NUMBER OF LAKES BY ECONOMIC REGION

Which economic region of Canada has the most lakes?

A Newfoundland and Maritime Provinces

B Quebec

C Prairie Provinces

D The North

Unit 7

UNIT 7 | **DAILY FOCUS SKILLS**
Chapter 18 | **TRANSPARENCY 18-2**

ANSWER: No; During the War of 1812, Canada, as a British colony, was attacked by the United States.

Teacher Tip: Explain that time lines help us understand the order of historical events.

Interpreting Information on Time Lines

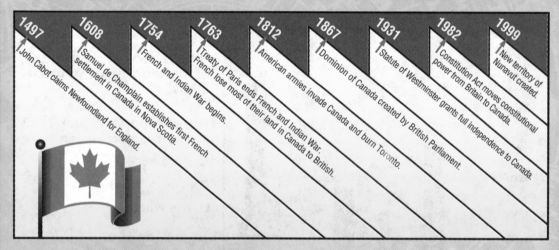

1497 John Cabot claims Newfoundland for England.

1608 Samuel de Champlain establishes first French settlement in Canada in Nova Scotia.

1754 French and Indian War begins.

1763 Treaty of Paris ends French and Indian War. French lose most of their land in Canada to British.

1812 American armies invade Canada and burn Toronto.

1867 Dominion of Canada created by British Parliament.

1931 Statute of Westminster grants full independence to Canada.

1982 Constitution Act moves constitutional power from Britain to Canada.

1999 New territory of Nunavut created.

Directions: Answer the following question based on the time line.

Have the United States and Canada always been allies? Explain.

_____

_____

Name _____ Date _____ Class _____

DAILY FOCUS SKILLS TRANSPARENCIES

Transparency 18-2

Interpreting Information on Time Lines

Directions: Answer the following question based on the time line in the space provided.

Have the United States and Canada always been allies? Explain.

_____

_____

Unit 7

Section 19-1

UNIT 7 | **DAILY FOCUS SKILLS**
Chapter 19 | **TRANSPARENCY 19-1**

ANSWER: D

Teacher Tip: Explain to students that the grid lines help to visually compare the height of the various mountain peaks.

Interpreting Graphs

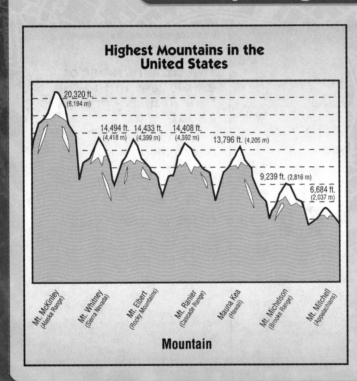

Highest Mountains in the United States

Directions: Answer the following question based on the graph.

What is the highest point in the Appalachian Mountains?

A Mt. Elbert

B Mt. Ranier

C Mt. Michelson

D Mt. Mitchell

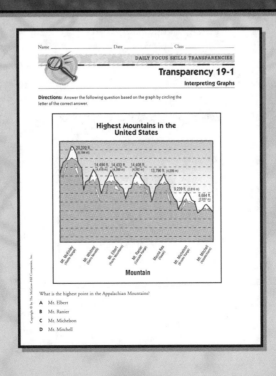

Unit 7

Section 19-2

UNIT 7 | **DAILY FOCUS SKILLS**
Chapter 19 | **TRANSPARENCY 19-2**

ANSWER: C

Teacher Tip: Explain to students that the numbers above the bars are the actual numbers of employees in the various industry groups.

Analyzing Graphs

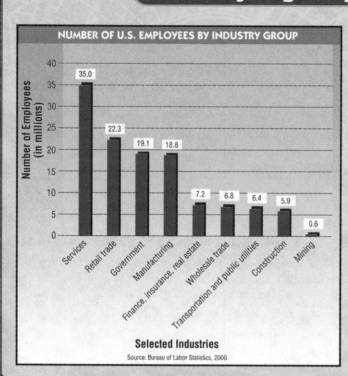

NUMBER OF U.S. EMPLOYEES BY INDUSTRY GROUP

Number of Employees (in millions)

Services 35.0
Retail trade 22.3
Government 19.1
Manufacturing 18.8
Finance, insurance, real estate 7.2
Wholesale trade 6.8
Transportation and public utilities 6.4
Construction 5.9
Mining 0.6

Selected Industries

Source: Bureau of Labor Statistics, 2000.

Directions: Answer the following question based on the bar graph.

The total number of employees in the top four industry groups is about

A 57 million.

B 77 million.

C 95 million.

D 122 million.

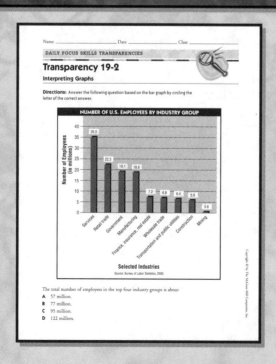

Name _____ Date _____ Class _____

DAILY FOCUS SKILLS TRANSPARENCIES

Transparency 19-2

Interpreting Graphs

Directions: Answer the following question based on the bar graph by circling the letter of the correct answer.

NUMBER OF U.S. EMPLOYEES BY INDUSTRY GROUP

Selected Industries

Source: Bureau of Labor Statistics, 2000.

The total number of employees in the top four industry groups is about
A   57 million.
B   77 million.
C   95 million.
D   122 million.

Unit 7

Section 19-3

UNIT 7 | **DAILY FOCUS SKILLS**
Chapter 19 | **TRANSPARENCY 19-3**

ANSWER: A

Teacher Tip: Encourage students to use a dictionary to look up the definition of any word they do not know.

Using Secondary Sources

"The mouth of the cave was up the hillside.... Within was a small chamber, chilly as an icehouse, and walled by Nature with solid limestone that was dewy with a cold sweat.... By and by the procession went filing down the steep descent of the main avenue, the flickering rank of lights dimly revealing the lofty walls of rock.... This main avenue was not more than eight or ten feet wide. Every few steps other lofty and still narrower crevices branched from it on either hand—for McDougal's cave was but a vast labyrinth of crooked aisles that ran into each other and out again and led nowhere.... No man 'knew' the cave. That was an impossible thing...."

—from *The Adventures of Tom Sawyer* by Mark Twain

Directions: Answer the following question based on the reading.

From Mark Twain's description, the cave can best be described as

A cold and damp.

B warm and damp.

C cold and dry.

D warm and dry.

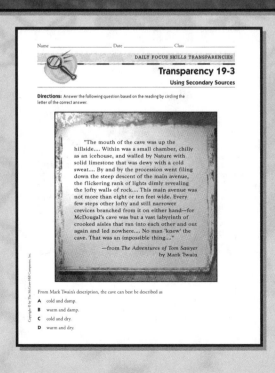

Name _____ Date _____ Class _____

DAILY FOCUS SKILLS TRANSPARENCIES

Transparency 19-3
Using Secondary Sources

Directions: Answer the following question based on the reading by circling the letter of the correct answer.

"The mouth of the cave was up the hillside.... Within was a small chamber, chilly as an icehouse, and walled by Nature with solid limestone that was dewy with a cold sweat.... By and by the procession went filing down the steep descent of the main avenue, the flickering rank of lights dimly revealing the lofty walls of rock.... This main avenue was not more than eight or ten feet wide. Every few steps other lofty and still narrower crevices branched from it on either hand—for McDougal's cave was but a vast labyrinth of crooked aisles that ran into each other and out again and led nowhere.... No man 'knew' the cave. That was an impossible thing...."

—from *The Adventures of Tom Sawyer* by Mark Twain

From Mark Twain's description, the cave can best be described as

A cold and damp.

B warm and damp.

C cold and dry.

D warm and dry.

Copyright © by The McGraw-Hill Companies, Inc.

Section 20-1

UNIT 7 | **DAILY FOCUS SKILLS**
Chapter 20 | **TRANSPARENCY 20-1**

ANSWER: A

Teacher Tip: The average temperature for any day is found by adding the high temperature and the low temperature and dividing the sum by 2.

Interpreting Tables

Mexico City, Mexico				Latitude: 19°N				Elevation: 7,347 ft. (2,239 m)			
Month	Jan.	Feb.	Mar.	Apr.	May	June	July	Aug.	Sept.	Oct.	Nov.	Dec.
Average Temperature*	57°	59°	63°	66°	67°	67°	65°	65°	64°	63°	60°	58°
Highest Recorded Temperature*	86°	84°	88°	88°	91°	91°	86°	86°	86°	86°	91°	88°
Lowest Recorded Temperature*	26°	30°	28°	34°	36°	43°	37°	43°	36°	36°	33°	28°

Monterrey, Mexico				Latitude: 25°N				Elevation: 1,752 ft. (534 m)			
Month	Jan.	Feb.	Mar.	Apr.	May	June	July	Aug.	Sept.	Oct.	Nov.	Dec.
Average Temperature*	58°	62°	70°	76°	80°	84°	84°	85°	80°	74°	66°	60°
Highest Recorded Temperature*	95°	100°	108°	111°	109°	111°	109°	106°	102°	102°	99°	95°
Lowest Recorded Temperature*	32°	32°	34°	37°	36°	59°	59°	54°	54°	43°	34°	32°

*Temperatures in Fahrenheit

Directions: Answer the following question based on the table.

During which month are the average temperatures in these two Mexican cities most similar?

A January

B March

C July

D December

Name _____ Date _____ Class _____

DAILY FOCUS SKILLS TRANSPARENCIES

Transparency 20-1
Interpreting Tables

Directions: Answer the following question based on the table by circling the letter of the correct answer.

Mexico City, Mexico				Latitude: 19°N				Elevation: 7,347 ft. (2,239 m)			
Month	Jan.	Feb.	Mar.	Apr.	May	June	July	Aug.	Sept.	Oct.	Nov.	Dec.
Average Temperature*	57°	59°	63°	66°	67°	67°	65°	65°	64°	63°	60°	58°
Highest Recorded Temperature*	86°	84°	88°	88°	91°	91°	86°	86°	86°	86°	91°	88°
Lowest Recorded Temperature*	26°	30°	28°	34°	36°	43°	37°	43°	36°	36°	33°	28°

Monterrey, Mexico				Latitude: 25°N				Elevation: 1,752 ft. (534 m)			
Month	Jan.	Feb.	Mar.	Apr.	May	June	July	Aug.	Sept.	Oct.	Nov.	Dec.
Average Temperature*	58°	62°	70°	76°	80°	84°	84°	85°	80°	74°	66°	60°
Highest Recorded Temperature*	95°	100°	108°	111°	109°	111°	109°	106°	102°	102°	99°	95°
Lowest Recorded Temperature*	32°	32°	34°	37°	36°	59°	59°	54°	54°	43°	34°	32°

*Temperatures in Fahrenheit

During which month are the average temperatures in these two Mexican cities most similar?

A January

B March

C July

D December

Unit 7

Section 20-2

UNIT 7 | **DAILY FOCUS SKILLS**
Chapter 20 | **TRANSPARENCY 20-2**

ANSWER: C

Teacher Tip: Explain to students that statements of opinion often include key words such as *should, best, all, every,* or *always.*

Distinguishing Fact From Opinion

1. Native Americans lived in Mexico long before European explorers arrived.

2. The Mayan culture developed ways to measure time accurately.

3. The Mayan civilization declined because the people were always fighting.

4. The Aztec Empire was larger and greater than the Mayan Empire.

5. The majority of Mexicans today have mixed Spanish and Native American heritage.

Directions: Answer the following question based on the sentences.

Which of the statements are facts?

A 1, 2, and 3

B 3, 4, and 5

C 1, 2, and 5

D 1, 3, and 5

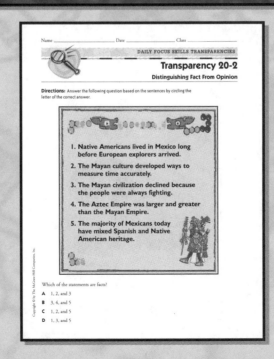

Name _____ Date _____ Class _____

DAILY FOCUS SKILLS TRANSPARENCIES

Transparency 20-2

Distinguishing Fact From Opinion

Directions: Answer the following question based on the sentences by circling the letter of the correct answer.

1. Native Americans lived in Mexico long before European explorers arrived.

2. The Mayan culture developed ways to measure time accurately.

3. The Mayan civilization declined because the people were always fighting.

4. The Aztec Empire was larger and greater than the Mayan Empire.

5. The majority of Mexicans today have mixed Spanish and Native American heritage.

Which of the statements are facts?

A 1, 2, and 3
B 3, 4, and 5
C 1, 2, and 5
D 1, 3, and 5

Copyright © by The McGraw-Hill Companies, Inc.

Unit 7

Section 20-3

UNIT 7 | **DAILY FOCUS SKILLS**
Chapter 20 | **TRANSPARENCY 20-3**

ANSWER: C

Teacher Tip: Many product labels are now written in English with Spanish translations. Bring labels to class for practice in translating.

Analyzing Information

Directions: Answer the following question based on the drawings and Spanish terms.

Which of the following terms would you most likely find on a breakfast menu?

A pimienta cayena

B frijoles

C huevos

D pollo

Name _____ Date _____ Class _____

DAILY FOCUS SKILLS TRANSPARENCIES

Transparency 20-3

Analyzing Information

Directions: Answer the following question based on the drawings and Spanish terms by circling the letter of the correct answer.

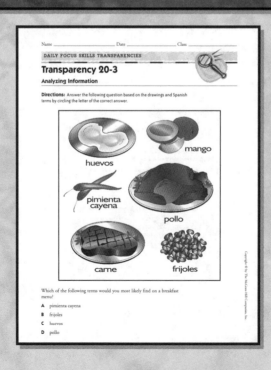

Which of the following terms would you most likely find on a breakfast menu?

A pimienta cayena

B frijoles

C huevos

D pollo

Unit 7

Section 21-1

UNIT 7 | **DAILY FOCUS SKILLS**
Chapter 21 | **TRANSPARENCY 21-1**

ANSWER: B

Teacher Tip: Tell students that the length of the bars indicates the literacy percentage in each country. The length of the bars can be used to make quick comparisons among the countries.

Reading a Bar Graph

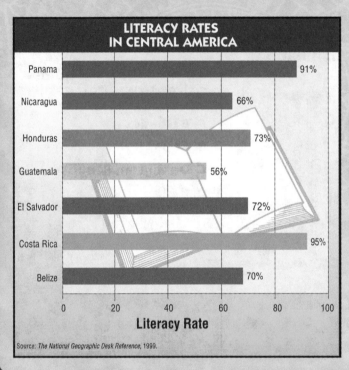

LITERACY RATES IN CENTRAL AMERICA

Country	Literacy Rate
Panama	91%
Nicaragua	66%
Honduras	73%
Guatemala	56%
El Salvador	72%
Costa Rica	95%
Belize	70%

Literacy Rate

Source: *The National Geographic Desk Reference*, 1999.

Directions: Answer the following question based on the bar graph.

Which country has the highest literacy rate in Central America?

A Belize

B Costa Rica

C Honduras

D Panama

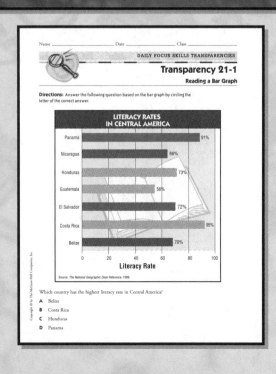

Name _____ Date _____ Class _____

DAILY FOCUS SKILLS TRANSPARENCIES

Transparency 21-1
Reading a Bar Graph

Directions: Answer the following question based on the bar graph by circling the letter of the correct answer.

LITERACY RATES IN CENTRAL AMERICA

Country	Literacy Rate
Panama	91%
Nicaragua	66%
Honduras	73%
Guatemala	56%
El Salvador	72%
Costa Rica	95%
Belize	70%

Literacy Rate

Source: *The National Geographic Desk Reference*, 1999.

Which country has the highest literacy rate in Central America?

A Belize
B Costa Rica
C Honduras
D Panama

Unit 7

UNIT 7 | **DAILY FOCUS SKILLS**
Chapter 21 | **TRANSPARENCY 21-2**

ANSWER: C

Teacher Tip: Compare and contrast the voting facts for these countries with voting rights in the United States.

Analyzing Information

The right to vote gives citizens a voice in the political decisions of a nation.

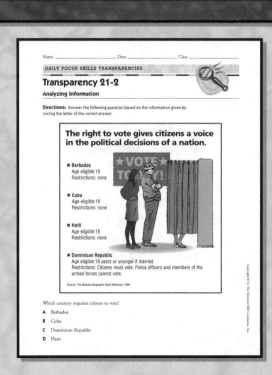

- **Barbados**
  Age eligible:18
  Restrictions: none

- **Cuba**
  Age eligible:16
  Restrictions: none

- **Haiti**
  Age eligible:18
  Restrictions: none

- **Dominican Republic**
  Age eligible:18 years or younger if married
  Restrictions: Citizens must vote. Police officers and members of the armed forces cannot vote.

Source: *The National Geographic Desk Reference,* 1999.

Directions: Answer the following question based on the information given.

Which country requires citizens to vote?

A Barbados

B Cuba

C Dominican Republic

D Haiti

Name _____ Date _____ Class _____

DAILY FOCUS SKILLS TRANSPARENCIES

Transparency 21-2

Analyzing Information

Directions: Answer the following question based on the information given by circling the letter of the correct answer.

The right to vote gives citizens a voice in the political decisions of a nation.

- **Barbados**
  Age eligible:18
  Restrictions: none

- **Cuba**
  Age eligible:16
  Restrictions: none

- **Haiti**
  Age eligible:18
  Restrictions: none

- **Dominican Republic**
  Age eligible:18 years or younger if married
  Restrictions: Citizens must vote. Police officers and members of the armed forces cannot vote.

Source: *The National Geographic Desk Reference,* 1999.

Which country requires citizens to vote?

A Barbados

B Cuba

C Dominican Republic

D Haiti

Unit 8

Section 22-1

UNIT 8 **DAILY FOCUS SKILLS**
Chapter 22 **TRANSPARENCY 22-1**

ANSWER: C

Teacher Tip: Remind students that a circle graph shows how 100 percent of something (in this case, Brazil's population) is divided among parts.

Interpreting Circle Graphs

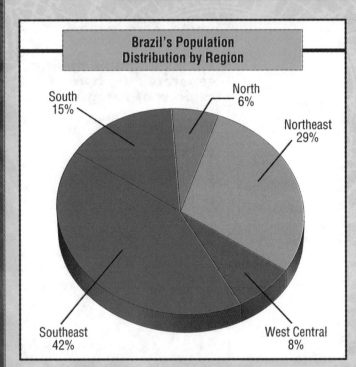

Brazil's Population Distribution by Region

North 6%

Northeast 29%

South 15%

Southeast 42%

West Central 8%

Directions: Answer the following question based on the circle graph.

Which region of Brazil has the largest population?

A Northeast

B South

C Southeast

D West Central

Name _____ Date _____ Class _____

DAILY FOCUS SKILLS TRANSPARENCIES

Transparency 22-1
Interpreting Circle Graphs

Directions: Answer the following question based on the circle graph by circling the letter of the correct answer.

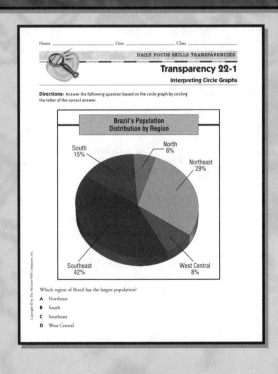

Brazil's Population Distribution by Region

North 6%

South 15%

Northeast 29%

Southeast 42%

West Central 8%

Which region of Brazil has the largest population?

A Northeast

B South

C Southeast

D West Central

Copyright © by The McGraw-Hill Companies, Inc.

Unit 8

Section 22-2

UNIT 8 | **DAILY FOCUS SKILLS**
Chapter 22 | **TRANSPARENCY 22-2**

ANSWER: B

Teacher Tip: Explain to students that a compass rose is included on maps to reference the cardinal directions.

Interpreting Maps

Directions: Answer the following question based on the map.

What geographic feature separates the two regions of Paraguay?

A Bolivia/Brazil border

B Paraguay River

C Paraná River

D Tropic of Capricorn

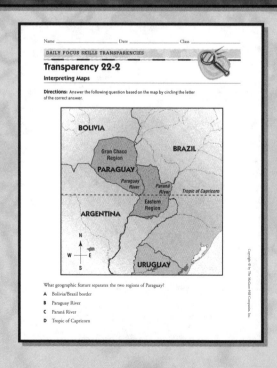

Name _____ Date _____ Class _____

DAILY FOCUS SKILLS TRANSPARENCIES

Transparency 22-2

Interpreting Maps

Directions: Answer the following question based on the map by circling the letter of the correct answer.

What geographic feature separates the two regions of Paraguay?

A Bolivia/Brazil border

B Paraguay River

C Paraná River

D Tropic of Capricorn

Unit 8

UNIT 8 | **DAILY FOCUS SKILLS**
Chapter 23 | **TRANSPARENCY 23-1**

ANSWER: B

Teacher Tip: Tell students that the map on the left shows the outline of Colombia with one area highlighted. The map on the right shows more detail of the highlighted area on the outline map.

Interpreting Maps

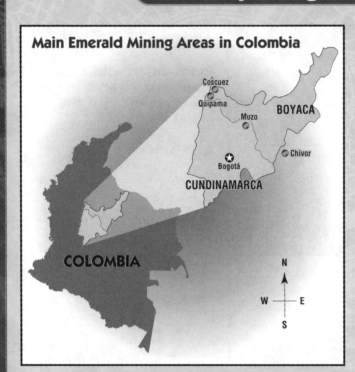

Main Emerald Mining Areas in Colombia

Directions: Answer the following question based on the maps.

Which mining area is farthest north?

A Chivor

B Coscuez

C Muzo

D Quipama

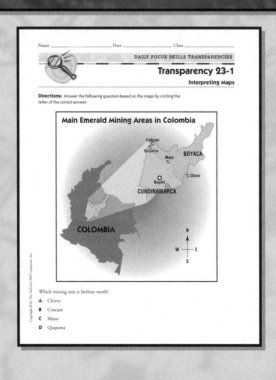

Name _____ Date _____ Class _____

DAILY FOCUS SKILLS TRANSPARENCIES

Transparency 23-1

Interpreting Maps

Directions: Answer the following question based on the maps by circling the letter of the correct answer.

Main Emerald Mining Areas in Colombia

Which mining area is farthest north?

A Chivor

B Coscuez

C Muzo

D Quipama

Unit 8

Section 23-2

UNIT 8 | **DAILY FOCUS SKILLS**
Chapter 23 | **TRANSPARENCY 23-2**

ANSWER: C

Teacher Tip: Explain to students that map keys help you understand the symbols and shading used on the map.

Interpreting Maps

Directions: Answer the following question based on the map.

From where did Spaniard Francisco Pizarro begin his invasion into the Incan Empire?

A Cajamarca

B Cuzco

C Portobelo

D Santiago

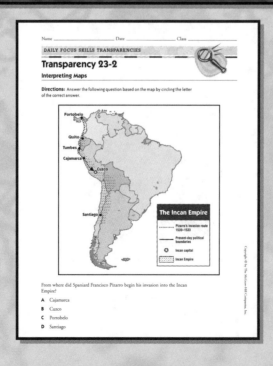

Unit 8

Section 23-3

UNIT 8 | **DAILY FOCUS SKILLS**
Chapter 23 | **TRANSPARENCY 23-3**

ANSWER: C

Teacher Tip: Tell students that *Other* often appears on graphs. On this graph it represents the tourists who come from all other countries.

Interpreting Bar Graphs

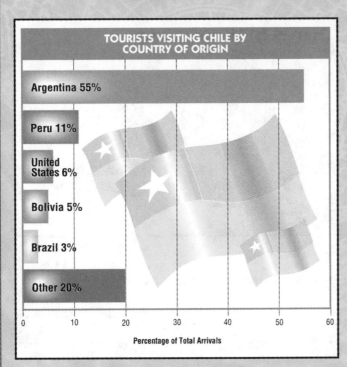

TOURISTS VISITING CHILE BY COUNTRY OF ORIGIN

Argentina 55%
Peru 11%
United States 6%
Bolivia 5%
Brazil 3%
Other 20%

Percentage of Total Arrivals

Directions: Answer the following question based on the graph.

The three countries that border Chile are Argentina, Bolivia, and Peru. What is the total percentage of tourists visiting Chile from these countries?

A 55%

B 66%

C 71%

D 74%

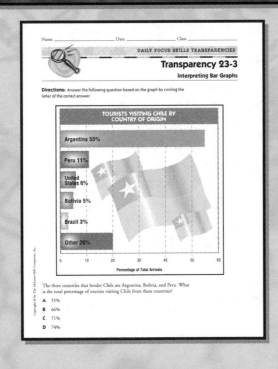

Name _____ Date _____ Class _____

DAILY FOCUS SKILLS TRANSPARENCIES

Transparency 23-3

Interpreting Bar Graphs

Directions: Answer the following question based on the graph by circling the letter of the correct answer.

TOURISTS VISITING CHILE BY COUNTRY OF ORIGIN

Argentina 55%
Peru 11%
United States 6%
Bolivia 5%
Brazil 3%
Other 20%

Percentage of Total Arrivals

The three countries that border Chile are Argentina, Bolivia, and Peru. What is the total percentage of tourists visiting Chile from these countries?

A 55%

B 66%

C 71%

D 74%

Unit 9

UNIT 9 | DAILY FOCUS SKILLS
Chapter 24 | TRANSPARENCY 24-1

ANSWER: Students may explain that the proper grip will allow the thrower to get the correct amount of spin on the boomerang so that it will return to the thrower. *Teacher Tip:* Tell students that one way to understand the diagram is to mimic the steps shown in the diagram.

Interpreting Diagrams

How to Throw a Boomerang

GRIP 1

GRIP 2

THROW

CATCH

Directions: Answer the following question based on the diagram.

Why do you think that the grip you use is important to the way you throw a boomerang?

_____

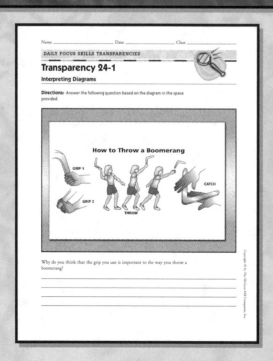

Section 24-2

UNIT 9 | **DAILY FOCUS SKILLS**
Chapter 24 | **TRANSPARENCY 24-2**

ANSWER: The chicks depart during the warmest months in Antarctica.

Teacher Tip: Remind students that the seasons in the southern hemisphere are opposite those in the northern hemisphere.

Interpreting Information on Tables

INTERNATIONAL ARRIVALS TO AND DEPARTURES FROM NEW ZEALAND			
Arrivals	**1997**	**1998**	**1999**
Visitors from other countries	1,541,340	1,458,210	1,539,230
Returning New Zealand residents	1,104,680	1,151,220	1,181,620
Immigrants to New Zealand from other countries	74,490	61,250	56,250
Total arrivals	2,720,510	2,670,680	2,777,100
Departures			
Visitors from other countries	1,526,780	1,461,220	1,544,880
New Zealand residents (leaving on short-term trips)	1,109,130	1,147,510	1,181,790
New Zealand residents emigrating (leaving permanently)	57,720	60,790	67,620
Total departures	2,693,630	2,669,520	2,794,290

Source: Profile of New Zealand 2000

Directions: Answer the following question based on the table.

Which of the following statements is accurate?

A The number of people visiting New Zealand from other countries has increased each year.

B Few New Zealand residents visit other countries.

C Most people who visit New Zealand do not move there permanently.

D Total arrivals are greater than total departures in all three years.

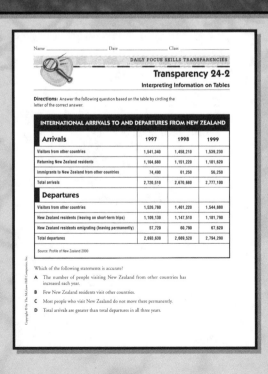

Name _____ Date _____ Class _____

DAILY FOCUS SKILLS TRANSPARENCIES

Transparency 24-2

Interpreting Information on Tables

Directions: Answer the following question based on the table by circling the letter of the correct answer.

INTERNATIONAL ARRIVALS TO AND DEPARTURES FROM NEW ZEALAND			
Arrivals	1997	1998	1999
Visitors from other countries	1,541,340	1,458,210	1,539,230
Returning New Zealand residents	1,104,680	1,151,220	1,181,620
Immigrants to New Zealand from other countries	74,490	61,250	56,250
Total arrivals	2,720,510	2,670,680	2,777,100
Departures			
Visitors from other countries	1,526,780	1,461,220	1,544,880
New Zealand residents (leaving on short-term trips)	1,109,130	1,147,510	1,181,790
New Zealand residents emigrating (leaving permanently)	57,720	60,790	67,620
Total departures	2,693,630	2,669,520	2,794,290

Source: Profile of New Zealand 2000

Which of the following statements is accurate?

A The number of people visiting New Zealand from other countries has increased each year.

B Few New Zealand residents visit other countries.

C Most people who visit New Zealand do not move there permanently.

D Total arrivals are greater than total departures in all three years.

Copyright © by The McGraw-Hill Companies, Inc.

Unit 9

UNIT 9 | **DAILY FOCUS SKILLS**
Chapter 25 | **TRANSPARENCY 25-1**

ANSWER: C

Teacher Tip: Remind students to use the compass rose to orient themselves to the directions on a map.

Interpreting Maps

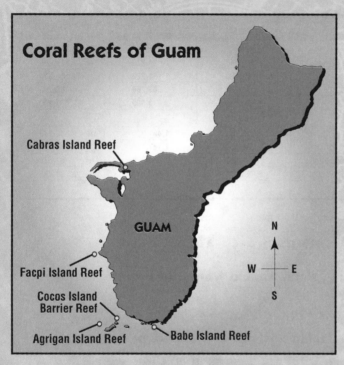

Coral Reefs of Guam

Cabras Island Reef

GUAM

Facpi Island Reef

Cocos Island Barrier Reef

Agrigan Island Reef   Babe Island Reef

N
W   E
S

Directions: Answer the following question based on the map.

Which coral reef is farthest north?

A Agrigan Island Reef

B Babe Island Reef

C Cabras Island Reef

D Cocos Island Barrier Reef

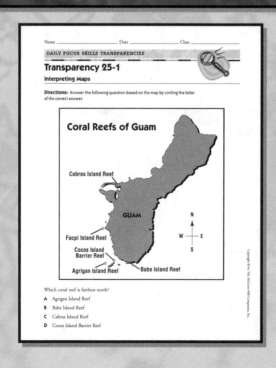

Name _____ Date _____ Class _____

DAILY FOCUS SKILLS TRANSPARENCIES

Transparency 25-1

Interpreting Maps

Directions: Answer the following question based on the map by circling the letter of the correct answer.

Coral Reefs of Guam

Cabras Island Reef

GUAM

Facpi Island Reef

Cocos Island Barrier Reef

Agrigan Island Reef   Babe Island Reef

N
W   E
S

Which coral reef is farthest north?

A   Agrigan Island Reef

B   Babe Island Reef

C   Cabras Island Reef

D   Cocos Island Barrier Reef

Unit 9

Section 25-2

Copyright © by The McGraw-Hill Companies, Inc.

UNIT 9 | **DAILY FOCUS SKILLS**
Chapter 25 | **TRANSPARENCY 25-2**

ANSWER: The chicks depart during the warmest months in Antarctica.

Teacher Tip: Explain to students that a generalization is a basic idea that can be formed from a set of facts.

Making Generalizations

Adelie and Emperor Penguins of Antarctica

	Adelie Penguins	Emperor Penguins
Size	29.5" (75 cm)	47" (120 cm)
Maximum weight	14 lbs. (6.5 kg)	99 lbs. (45 kg)
Egg laying	November	May
Hatching	December	July
Chicks depart	February	December/January
Main food	Krill	Squid and fish

Directions: Answer the following question based on the information about Adelie and Emperor penguins.

Why do you think both species of penguins have chicks departing the nest in December through February?

_____

_____

_____

_____

Name _____ Date _____ Class _____

DAILY FOCUS SKILLS TRANSPARENCIES

Transparency 25-2

Making Generalizations

Directions: Answer the following question based on the information about Adelie and Emperor penguins in the space provided.

Adelie and Emperor Penguins of Antarctica

	Adelie Penguins	Emperor Penguins
Size	29.5" (75 cm)	47" (120 cm)
Maximum weight	14 lbs. (6.5 kg)	99 lbs. (45 kg)
Egg laying	November	May
Hatching	December	July
Chicks depart	February	December/January
Main food	Krill	Squid and fish

Why do you think both species of penguins have chicks departing the nest in December through February?

_____
_____

Copyright © by The McGraw-Hill Companies, Inc.

11 Political Map Transparencies

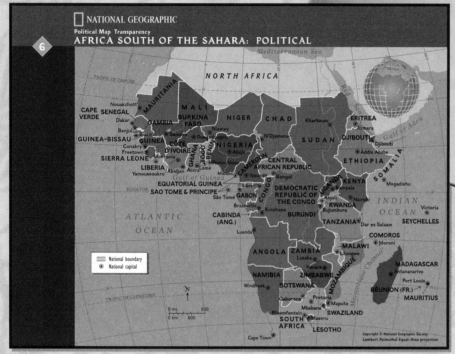

NATIONAL GEOGRAPHIC
Political Map Transparency
AFRICA SOUTH OF THE SAHARA: POLITICAL

*T*he **Teaching Transparencies Sampler** for *Our World Today* includes:

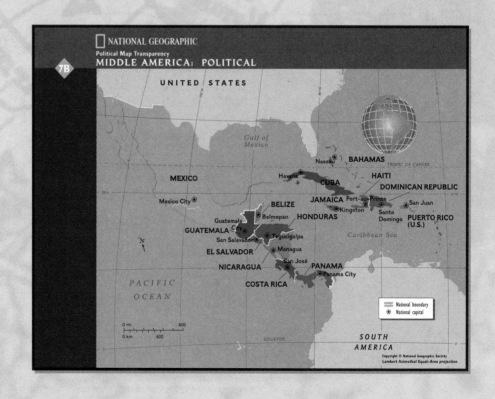

NATIONAL GEOGRAPHIC
Political Map Transparency
MIDDLE AMERICA: POLITICAL

TRANSPARENCIES SAMPLER!

71 Map Overlay Transparencies

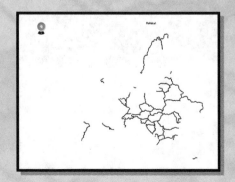

MORE TEACHING

16 World Cultures Transparencies

NATIONAL GEOGRAPHIC
World Cultures Transparency
1 NORTH AFRICA AND SOUTHWEST ASIA

© Richard Pasley/Stock, Boston/PictureQuest

Making a Living in Morocco

A Moroccan businessman glimmers in the golden hue of his brass shop amid pots, pans, candlesticks, and lamps.

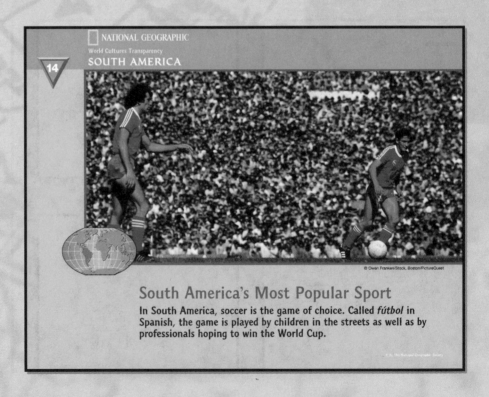

NATIONAL GEOGRAPHIC
World Cultures Transparency
14 SOUTH AMERICA

© Owen Franken/Stock, Boston/PictureQuest

South America's Most Popular Sport

In South America, soccer is the game of choice. Called *fútbol* in Spanish, the game is played by children in the streets as well as by professionals hoping to win the World Cup.

TRANSPARENCIES!

9 Geography Handbook Transparencies

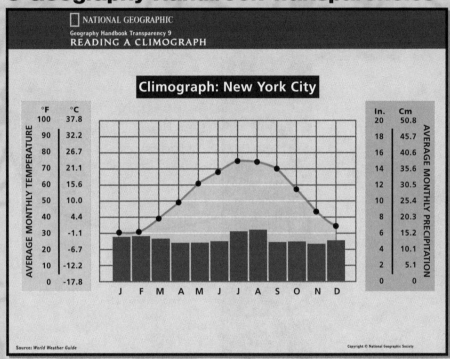

NATIONAL GEOGRAPHIC
Geography Handbook Transparency 9
READING A CLIMOGRAPH

Climograph: New York City

Source: *World Weather Guide*

Copyright © National Geographic Society

15 Graphic Organizer Transparencies

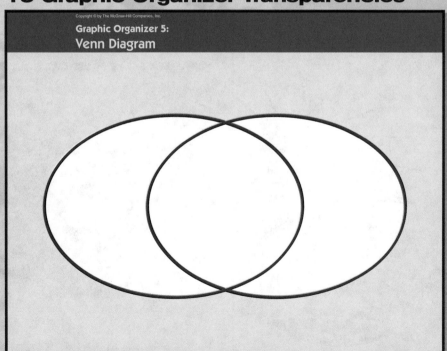

Copyright © by The McGraw-Hill Companies, Inc.

Graphic Organizer 5:
Venn Diagram

There's a
GeoQuiz Transparencies
Sampler, too!

56 GeoQuiz Transparencies

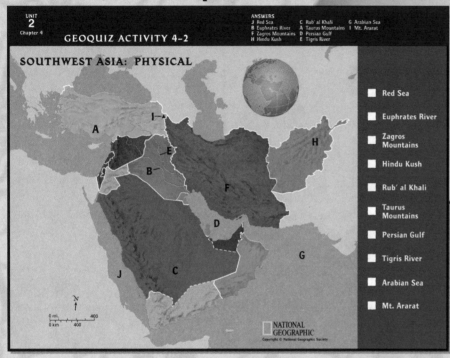

The **GeoQuiz Transparencies Sampler** for *Our World Today* includes:

This Sampler includes 4 actual Daily Focus Skills Transparencies that you can use in your World Cultures classroom. Order the entire set from Glencoe!

THOSE WHO CARE—
TEACH!